GNOMES

AND

GARDENS

dedicated to aline and nick, and
lorna, the snails' friend

► a note about the ◄
author and illustrator

Nigel Suckling and Wayne Anderson are two seasoned
(as opposed to just wizened) English investigators who
have spent over half their lives pursuing fairies,
dragons, unicorns and just about every other fantastic
creature you can think of. That most people believe they
don't exist has so far proved no great obstacle.

In this book they turn their attention to that most homely
and down to earth of the fairy people, the common or
garden gnome; throwing fresh light on a misunderstood
race that has lived alongside humans since time began.
Not least of their discoveries is that gnomes continue to
thrive happily in the modern world and are as easily found
as ever by those who know where (and how) to look.

GNOMES AND GARDENS

a field guide to the

little people

NIGEL SUCKLING

ILLUSTRATED BY WAYNE ANDERSON

PAVILION

First published in Great Britain in 2000 by
PAVILION BOOKS LIMITED
London House, Great Eastern Wharf
Parkgate Road, London SW11 4NQ

Text © Nigel Suckling 2000
Illustrations © Wayne Anderson 2000
Games © Nigel Suckling 2000
Design and layout © Pavilion Books Ltd 2000

The moral right of the author and illustrator
has been asserted

Designed by Sian Rance and David Costa at Wherefore Art?

A CIP catalogue record for this book is available
from the British Library.

ISBN 1 86205 4258

Set in Amigo and Freakshow Real Scary
Manufactured in China by Imago
Colour reproduction by Bright Arts, Hong Kong

2 4 6 8 10 9 7 5 3 1

This book can be ordered direct from the publisher. Please contact the
Marketing Department. But try your bookshop first.

► contents ◄

introduction

GNOMES ARE A HOMELY BREED OF ELF THAT HAVE LIVED HAPPILY – AND MOSTLY INVISIBLY – ALONGSIDE HUMANS SINCE WE CAME DOWN FROM THE TREES, AND SOME WOULD SAY MUCH LONGER.

DOWN THE AGES THEY HAVE COME TO SHARE MANY OF OUR HABITS AND TASTES. MOST GNOMES, FOR INSTANCE, HAVE A PENCHANT FOR ORDER IN THEIR LIVES AND PREFER TO BE LEFT TO GET ON WITH THINGS AT THEIR OWN PACE. THEY LIKE A FULL LARDER AND LOG-PILE AND BEING FREE TO TEND THEIR GARDENS WITHOUT A RUSH. SOMETIMES THEY LIKE TIME TO DO NOTHING AT ALL BUT SIMPLY ENJOY BEING ALIVE. WHERE GNOMES DIFFER MAINLY FROM US IS THAT ON THE WHOLE THEY ARE FAR LESS AMBITIOUS, FAR MORE IN TUNE WITH THE NATURAL WORLD AND FAR MORE EASILY CONTENT WITH WHAT FATE THROWS THEIR WAY.

GNOMES ARE MOSTLY FAR HAPPIER WITH THEIR LIVES THAN WE ARE, AND FIND IT MUCH EASIER TO RELAX AT THE END OF THEIR DAY. THEY SAY THE TROUBLE WITH HUMANS IS THAT WE SPEND AT LEAST HALF OUR LIVES WISHING WE WERE SOMEWHERE ELSE AND DOING SOMETHING TOTALLY DIFFERENT. WE RARELY MORE THAN HALF CONCENTRATE ON WHAT WE ARE ACTUALLY DOING AT THE TIME AND SO CAN ONLY HALF RELAX AFTERWARDS, BECAUSE WE'RE IMMEDIATELY RESTLESS TO BE GOING ON TO SOMETHING ELSE. GNOMES TEND TO DO EVERYTHING WHOLEHEARTEDLY, WHICH MAKES THEIR LIVES FAR SIMPLER AND MORE SATISFYING.

HERE WE SEE A GNOME RELAXING AFTER A BUSY DAY IN THE HOP FIELDS. BECAUSE THEY ARE ONLY GROWN IN CERTAIN AREAS, HOPS ARE ONE OF THE MORE COMMON HERBS THAT GNOMES TRADE AMONG THEMSELVES. THEY ARE ALSO NOT SHY ABOUT HELPING THEMSELVES TO SUPPLIES FROM HUMAN BREWERIES, REPAYING THE LOAN BY PLACING CHARMS ON THE BREW TO BRING ITS FLAVOUR TO LIFE. WISE BREWERS TURN A BLIND EYE TO SUCH 'BORROWINGS' BECAUSE THEY KNOW THAT IN THE LONG RUN THEY ONLY BENEFIT FROM IT. THE WISEST BREWERS PUT A GARDEN GNOME STATUE ON SHOW SOMEWHERE TO ENCOURAGE THE REAL ONES IN.

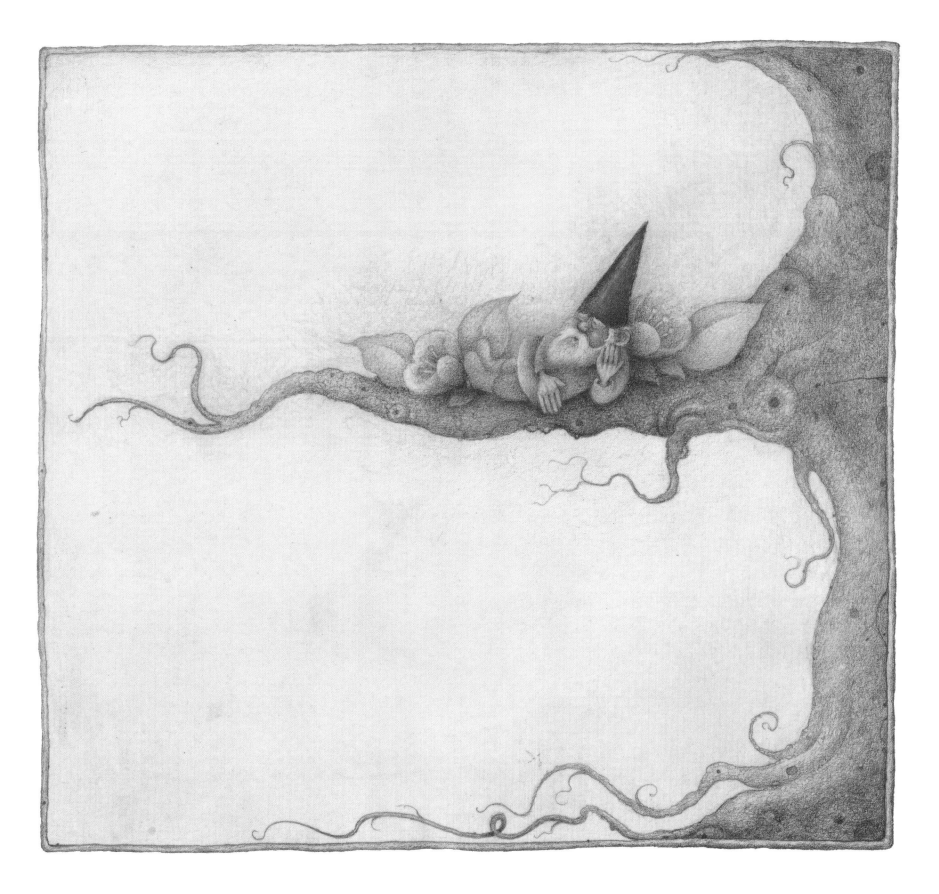

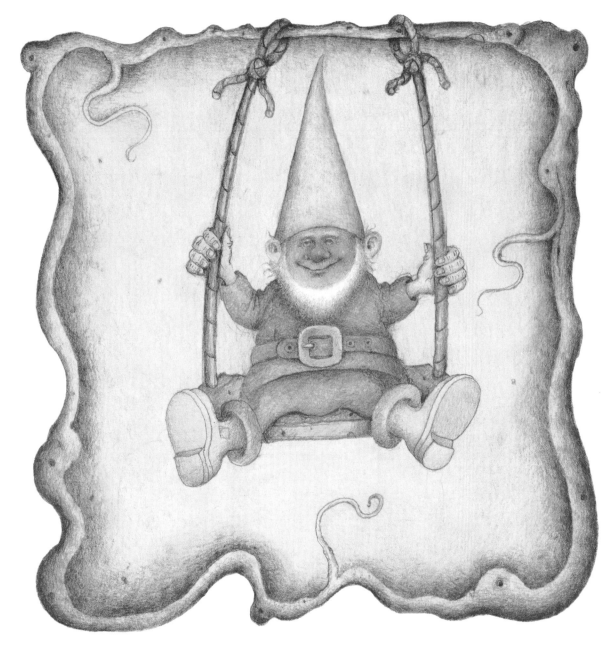

There are exceptions. There have been gnomes who have grown fabulously rich and lived in palaces. There have been others who have set out to conquer the world, though so far with a total lack of success, unless one believes some of the ancient Nordic legends about their exploits at the dawn of time. Whatever the case in the past, most gnomes these days live quiet, unassuming lives that help them escape our attention.

In GNOMES AND GARDENS we look at every aspect of gnome life that we have been able to uncover. We examine their origins and fashions, their hobbies and games and tastes. We look at gnomes who live in cities, suburbs and the countryside. We show a few examples of their home building and, of course, say something about their approach to gardening. Finally we have included a unique gnome board game, with rules for two of the simpler games that they play upon it.

Before we begin, though, there is one point that needs clearing up. There has been much speculation about the size of gnomes. They are most commonly said to be between six and eight inches (15–20 cm) tall, but people have also met much larger or smaller gnomes, particularly if one goes back in the records a couple of hundred years to when sightings were far more common than they are today. The explanation, we have found, is quite simple: the size of gnomes is not fixed.

A few gnomes can simply change their size at will, but for most it depends entirely on where they live. The reasons for this are obscure. The closest we could get to an explanation is that it is something to do with a kind of magnetic flux in the ground where they happen to live. Gnomes were originally born from the earth and are still intimately bound to it, far more so than humans, so these things affect them that much more.

GNOMES ENJOY SIMPLE PLEASURES. ENTERTAINMENTS THAT ONLY KEEP US DISTRACTED FOR A FEW YEARS OF OUR CHILDHOOD KEEP THEM AMUSED FOR MOST OF THEIR LIVES. AS A RESULT GNOME PARENTS AND CHILDREN HAVE FAR MORE IN COMMON THAN WE DO. IT IS FAR LESS HARD TO FIND SOMETHING THEY BOTH WANT TO DO. PERHAPS THIS IS WHY GNOMES HAVE NEVER INVENTED SCHOOLS FOR THEIR CHILDREN. GNOME CHILDREN JUST HANG AROUND THEIR PARENTS, AND THEN THE PARENTS OF THEIR FRIENDS, AND BETWEEN NATURAL CURIOSITY AND PLAYING GAMES THEY LEARN ALL THEY NEED TO KNOW WHEN THEY GROW UP. IT IS ONLY ADULT GNOMES THAT GO TO SCHOOL, IF THEY WANT TO LEARN TO BE A WIZARD OR SOMETHING LIKE THAT.

'There have been gnomes who have grown fabulously rich and lived in palaces.'

Here we see portraits of King Berg and Queen Brunhilde of the Harz Mountains in Germany. They are drawn from contemporary portraits said to be very good likenesses, but as these were only the size of postage stamps some concession has had to be taken. They ruled a thriving gnome kingdom in the sixteenth century based on a trade in unicorn horns, which were plentiful in that region at the time. All their subject gnomes got tired of taking orders after a while though, so the whole thing was abandoned. For a while the king and queen lived on in their palace alone, but then they got bored and went to live simple lives in the forest with the rest. This is usually how gnome kingdoms end. More often they don't get started in the first place.

So in some areas gnomes grow no more than an inch or two while in others they can be as large as a human child. And the curious thing is that small gnomes who migrate to an area where much larger ones live will soon grow larger too, and vice versa. Their size is only fixed in relation to each other.

In tackling the subject, we have been only too aware that some of our findings may seem to clash with what others have said about gnomes, but no argument has been intended. Any differences are simply due to the fact that we have found other sources. Whenever you try to describe any group simply by observing or questioning the individuals you happen to meet, a certain amount of luck is involved.

Much depends on the reliability of your informants. If they say 'all gnomes do this' you are inclined to believe them unless you already happen to know better. It's a bit like if you have only ever met one Lithuanian: your view of their country will be highly influenced by what they say it is like in Lithuania. But you may happen to have met a rather strange Lithuanian. So, we may have made one or two sweeping generalisations that do not apply to gnomes everywhere.

We hope these are far outweighed by all the fresh discoveries that do apply throughout the gnome world.

'so in some areas gnomes grow no more than an inch or two.'

GROWING UP IS A MUCH SMALLER PART OF GNOMES' LIVES THAN WITH US. THEY TAKE ABOUT TWICE AS LONG ABOUT IT BUT THEN THEY LIVE TO A VAST AGE, SO CHILDHOOD IS A MUCH SMALLER FRACTION OF THEIR LIVES. FROM WHEN THEY REACH MATURITY (AT ABOUT FIFTY), THE APPEARANCE OF GNOMES CHANGES ONLY VERY GRADUALLY TILL THEY REACH EXTREME OLD AGE. SO UNTIL WE GOT USED TO THIS, WE WERE OFTEN THROWN BY HEARING ONE GNOME ADDRESS ANOTHER AS 'GRANDAD' ALTHOUGH THEY LOOKED JUST LIKE BROTHERS. EXACTLY HOW ANCIENT GNOMES CAN GET REMAINS A BIT OF A MYSTERY, HOWEVER, BECAUSE NONE OF THEM WOULD TELL US. POSSIBLY THEY WERE JUST BEING POLITE AND SPARING OUR FEELINGS. IT WAS OFTEN ODD TALKING TO A GNOME 'CHILD' AND DISCOVERING WE WERE THE SAME AGE.

MUSHROOM BALANCING IS A POPULAR
GNOME SPORT. THE MUSHROOM ADDS AN
ELEMENT OF LUCK TO THE EVENT BECAUSE
NOT EVEN GNOMES CAN QUITE PREDICT
WHEN IT WILL WOBBLE AND SEND THEM
TUMBLING TO THE GROUND.

IT IS NOT JUST A SPORT, THOUGH. OFTEN
GNOMES ARE TESTING ITS STRENGTH AND
ELASTICITY, THOUGH WHAT BEARING THIS
HAS ON ANYTHING USEFUL WE NEVER
LEARNED. MUSHROOMS AND GNOMES HAVE
ALWAYS GONE TOGETHER. PEOPLE USED TO
BELIEVE GNOMES ACTUALLY LIVED IN THEM,
BUT THIS IS ONLY OCCASIONALLY TRUE. IT IS
MORE A ROUNDABOUT WAY OF SAYING THAT
IF YOU EAT CERTAIN MUSHROOMS YOU CAN
BE SURE OF SEEING GNOMES AND ANY OTHER
FAIRY CREATURE THAT HAPPENS TO BE
AROUND. WHICH IS AS TRUE TODAY AS IT
HAS EVER BEEN, THOUGH WE WOULD NOT
RECOMMEND IT UNLESS YOU HAPPEN TO
HAVE A GNOME HANDY TO ADVISE YOU ON
EXACTLY WHICH MUSHROOMS TO EAT AND
HOW MUCH. IN WHICH CASE THEY WOULD
NOT REALLY BE NEEDED, OF COURSE, BECAUSE
ONCE GNOMES HAVE ACCEPTED YOU, THERE IS
NO PROBLEM SEEING THEM.

IT ALSO USED TO BE BELIEVED THAT GNOMES
TURNED THEMSELVES INTO TOADSTOOLS
WHEN HUMANS CAME ALONG, AND THIS
APPARENTLY IS PERFECTLY TRUE. THEY DON'T
WAIT AROUND TO BE TRAMPLED ON,
HOWEVER. WITHIN THE TOADSTOOL THEY
BURROW DOWN AND ESCAPE UNDERGROUND.
THAT IS WHAT SOME OF THEM ASSURED US
ANYWAY, THOUGH THEY MAY HAVE BEEN
PULLING OUR LEGS.

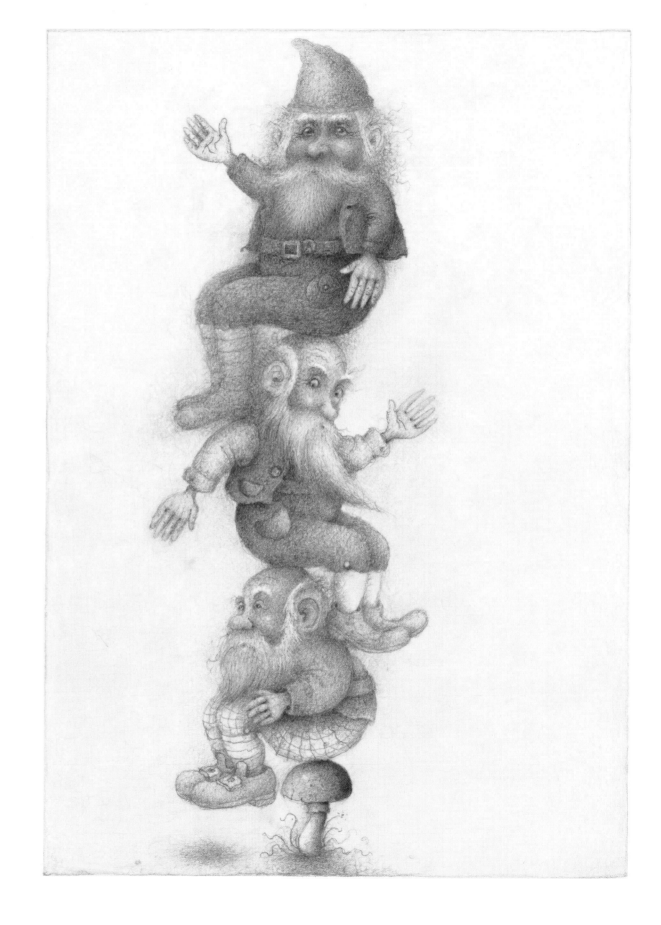

origins

GNOMES IN GENERAL DO NOT SEEM VERY INTERESTED IN

TO 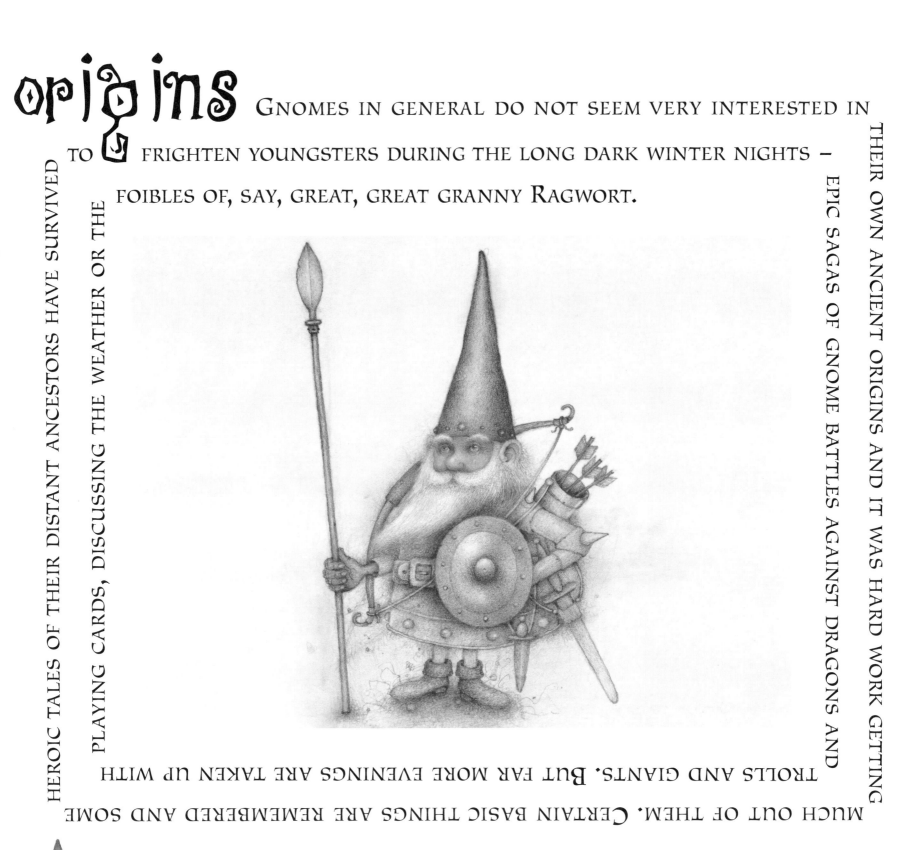 FRIGHTEN YOUNGSTERS DURING THE LONG DARK WINTER NIGHTS –

FOIBLES OF, SAY, GREAT, GREAT GRANNY RAGWORT.

THEIR OWN ANCIENT ORIGINS AND IT WAS HARD WORK GETTING

EPIC SAGAS OF GNOME BATTLES AGAINST DRAGONS AND

TROLLS AND GIANTS. BUT FAR MORE EVENINGS ARE TAKEN UP WITH

MUCH OUT OF THEM. CERTAIN BASIC THINGS ARE REMEMBERED AND SOME

HEROIC TALES OF THEIR DISTANT ANCESTORS HAVE SURVIVED

PLAYING CARDS, DISCUSSING THE WEATHER OR THE

'You know, the one who lived in
Dingley Dell and had twenty-one
children. Remember how she used to
line them up every now and then, bent
right over, and give them all a sound
thrashing. Used to say how they must all have
done some mischief since the last time and how
this saved her the bother of finding out exactly what
it was. What a card she was!'

Gnomes do, however, have some legends of the past that have
stood the test of time, and occasionally they will gather to hear
these read or recited by some passing wizard or storyteller. The
following is one that accounts for their origins and is familiar to most of
the gnomes you are ever likely to encounter.

gnomes and fairies
The father of all
gnomes, it is said, was a dwarf, one of those earth sprites that live entirely
underground, moving through earth and even solid rock as easily as a fish swims
through water. They dig tunnels like moles, but infinitely faster, and they continue to thrive to this
day. They are said to have invented smithcraft and taught it to the earliest humans. In ancient Crete
they were called dactyls and lived under Mount Ida. In Germany they forged the famous Ring of the
Nibelungs about which the epic drama of Siegfried revolves. They are often loosely called gnomes (just as
gnomes are often loosely called dwarves), but gnomes themselves draw a clear line between themselves and
dwarves, and you will see why.

Until modern times dwarves were familiar to human miners across Europe under a variety of names such as Knockers
in Cornwall and Mountain Monks in Bohemia. Today the din of modern mining drowns their presence, and in fact drives
them away completely because they can't stand it; but in the old days when mining was a slow and arduous grind, they could
often be heard tapping in some distant shaft. A certain kinship grew up between the humans and dwarves, engaged as they were
in similar pursuits. The human miners would often leave little presents behind at the end of their shift, and in return the sprites
would warn miners of impending cave-ins, gas and other disasters. Regularly also they would lead miners to promising veins of ore,
because, up to a point, they do not mind sharing the treasures of the earth.

These dwarves or earth sprites are all male. When one of them feels the need for a son, all he does is simply carve a fair likeness of himself out
of rock and then, after some complicated magic ritual known only to the dwarves themselves, a new dwarf is born.

Although descended from mining dwarves, very few gnomes choose to live underground more than they need to. Their hats are not very well suited for a start, but mostly it is the fresh air they miss. When they build homes underground they take care to allow for fresh draughts of air to run through them. Often in winter they light a fire as much for that as for keeping warm.

WHAT IS NOT CLEAR ABOUT THE WAY DWARVES REPRODUCE IS WHETHER THEY JUST PICK ANY OLD BIT OF ROCK LARGE ENOUGH FOR A STATUE, OR IF IT HAS TO BE A SPECIAL STONE WITH SOME STRANGE SPARK OF LIFE ALREADY IN IT. GNOMES THEMSELVES ARE NOT ALL AGREED BUT MOST BELIEVE IT HAS TO BE A SPECIAL STONE, A BIT LIKE THE ONES OUR ANCIENT ANCESTORS USED TO ARRANGE IN STONE CIRCLES, SENSING SOME POWER IN THEM.

Glob and Florabell

Dwarves spend all of their lives underground and so most of them can't bear the sunlight and fresh air of the outside world. But once, long ago, it is said that one of them did fall for these things. It came about when he happened by chance to come across a crack in the earth leading up to the outside. Down this cleft came the radiance of the moon like a wash of silver; a waft of warm air and, most importantly of all, the faint strains of an enchanting, elvish song that was sweeter than any song he had ever heard or imagined before. His curiosity pricked, the dwarf climbed up to investigate. His name varies according to the storyteller and the part of the world you are in, but he is often called Glob, so that will do.

Anyway, Glob climbed out of the crack into a moonlit night that dazzled his eyes because he was used to seeing only in the dark or by lamplight. Now, he had always been told that the outside world was ugly and empty and completely pointless, since the earth and rock out there were mostly covered with a blanket of soft, useless growing stuff. All this he found to be true, once his eyes had adjusted. The sky was vast and empty, its sparkling diamonds placed far beyond possible reach. The

rocks that are the dwarves' passion were smothered on every possible ledge by grass and bushes and trees. Yet to Glob's eyes there was a strange charm to the wooded valley that met his gaze that night, with its tinkling stream that tumbled down a rocky path through the midst of it. And there was strong enchantment, too, in the tune that came from some hidden singer in the trees below, a chiming magical song more delicate than Glob had ever heard before, being used only to the robust choruses of mining dwarves.

So Glob climbed out of the crack into the valley and went searching for the singer, marvelling as he went at the soft grass under his feet, speckled with flowers like living gems. He followed the sound till he came to a clearing where a strange creature sat on a large toadstool, singing. Soft and rounded, she was prettier than any dwarf dream. Startled, she looked round and their eyes met. It was love at first sight. Many people believe this only happens in fairytales, but not at all. It can just be an illusion. You meet someone who happens to remind you of someone else and your feelings just rush into the void. But sometimes it really is all your highest instincts rising to tell you that you have just met your soul mate.

GLOB WAS UNUSUAL IN FALLING
IN LOVE WITH A FAIRY. MOST
DWARVES AND EVEN GNOMES
FIND THEM A BIT ANAEMIC AND
LOOKING IN DIRE NEED OF A
GOOD HEARTY MEAL. ALSO FAIRIES
USUALLY LOOK VERY YOUNG AND
GNOMES LIKE TO SEE A BIT OF
CHARACTER IN A FACE. THIS IS
JUST AS WELL REALLY, BECAUSE
THEIR EXPERIENCE DOES SHOW
AND THEY CAN LIVE TO A VAST
AGE THAT WOULD BE WASTED IF
MOST OF IT WAS SPENT PINING
FOR THEIR LOST YOUTH.

AS WITH ALL PARENTS, GNOMES
MAKE SPECIAL ALLOWANCES FOR
THEIR CHILDREN, BUT SECRETLY
THEY ARE RATHER PLEASED FOR
THEM WHEN THEIR FIRST BEARDS
AND WRINKLES APPEAR.

'secretly they are rather pleased for their children when their first beards and wrinkles appear.'

Anyway, the long and short of it is that Glob fell in love with the fairy Florabell. And luckily she also fell in love with him. They took to meeting every night, and then sometimes even during the day. Slowly Glob grew to enjoy life in the open and lost his taste for the charms of the underworld. (He also found that he did not turn to stone at the touch of sunlight, which is something that all dwarves fear.) Finally they married and lived together in that little wooded valley and all the gnomes in the world believe they are descended from them, as much as people believe they come from Adam and Eve. Possibly more so, thinking about it.

Male gnomes look like softened versions of dwarves and females look like plumper, more solid versions of fairies. Occasionally they revert to kind. Male gnomes shoulder their picks and shovels and go back to living underground with the dwarves. And some female gnomes still occasionally sprout wings and (with a little help) fly away to join the fairies, but for the most part gnomes now live contentedly on the face of the earth, tending it and tilling it with the combined wisdom of their two species.

'some female gnomes still occasionally sprout wings and fly away to join the fairies.'

gnoman is an island

Gnomes originated in Northern Europe and are
related to most of the other known Little People of that
part of the world, such as the kobold of Germany, the
tomte or nisse of Scandinavia, the hobgoblin of England
and France, the brownie of northern Britain and the domoviye
of Russia. In fact, one could say that gnomes are a combination
of them all because if there was ever any great distinction between
the various Little People, it has largely dissolved through inter-
marriage. There do remain some regional variations. The piskies of
Cornwall, and especially the leprechauns of Ireland, have kept their own
identities even when living side by side with gnomes; and so have a few others,
but most kinds of Little People now seem to have merged into what we call
gnomes. Either that or they have become goblins.

Gnomes are also of course related to the Little People of Southern Europe, the Spanish
duende, Italian massariole or Greek pitikos, to about the same degree as the humans of those
parts are related. That is to say from the viewpoint of, say, China the differences are slight but
from the inside they can seem enormous. So to be on the safe side, anything we say about gnomes
should be taken to apply mainly to the northern variety.

In a wider sense gnomes are also related to all the other Little People of the world. They get along well
enough when they happen to meet, but their customs are so different it would be rash to extend anything we
say about gnomes in this book to other breeds of Little People. They have much in common, but how they express
their character is colourfully different in each case.

From northern Europe gnomes have spread to most other parts of the world, but their greatest numbers abroad are
probably in North America, parts of Australia and New Zealand. They tend to follow the drift of the humans from their
homelands, which shows how close they are to us really, but they are less keen than us on living in great cities. Some gnomes
do take to city life, but you will find far more in the suburbs and even more in the countryside beyond.

gnomophobia

In the old days when no one doubted their existence, there was some suspicion of the Little People. And to be honest it was often well deserved.
From Scotland there come countless tales of helpful brownies turning from doing useful little jobs around the house at night to making their hosts'
lives a misery, all because of some slight insult. You hear similar tales all across Europe and this is perhaps the main reason that gnomes like to simplify
their past, and distance themselves from their ancestors. If pressed, they will tell you that all serious mischief was the work of goblins (or gremlins; they
mean pretty much the same).

DISTINCTIONS BETWEEN THE VARIOUS LITTLE
PEOPLE OF EUROPE HAVE BEEN DISSOLVING
RAPIDLY FOR THE PAST FEW CENTURIES. SO YOU
ARE AS LIKELY TO MEET THIS FELLOW IN
MOLDAVIA AS IN CENTRAL FRANCE, WHICH IS
IN FACT WHERE WE DID MEET HIM BECAUSE
THAT IS AS FAR AS OUR BUDGET FOR
ORIGINAL RESEARCH STRETCHED. LANGUAGE
PROVED A BARRIER BECAUSE ALL HE SPOKE
(TO US ANYWAY) WAS A FRENCH DIALECT
THAT EVEN THE DORDOGNE LOCALS HAVE
ALMOST FORGOTTEN.

HE WAS AN AMIABLE ENOUGH COMPANION,
THOUGH, AND IT WAS STRANGELY REFRESHING
VIEWING THE STRANGE, TWISTED LANDSCAPE IN
HIS COMPANY. EVEN WITH BARELY A WORD
BEING EXCHANGED WE SEEMED TO SEE
THROUGH HIS EYES HOW IT HAD BEEN SHAPED
BY VIOLENT ERUPTIONS AND SPUMES OF LAVA
LONG AGO, AND HOW IT HAD BEEN GRADUALLY
SOFTENED AND TAMED BY NATURE EVER SINCE.

WHEN WE PARTED AT THE END IT FELT ALMOST
LIKE WAKING FROM A DREAM. THIS OFTEN
HAPPENS WHEN MEETING GNOMES BUT THE
FEELING WAS STRONGER IN THIS CASE. LATER
WE LEARNED THAT HE MUST HAVE BEEN A VERY
ANCIENT GNOME INDEED BECAUSE THEY OFTEN
LOSE INTEREST IN KEEPING UP WITH CHANGES
IN THEIR HUMAN NEIGHBOURS' WAY OF
TALKING. AMONG THEMSELVES GNOMES USE AN
ANCIENT AND SECRET LANGUAGE THEY ALL
UNDERSTAND, BUT ONLY FOR PROFOUND
THINGS. FOR TRIVIAL DAY-TO-DAY THINGS THEY
USE HUMAN SPEECH.

◀ A GNOME FROM KASHMIR. AS IN SWITZERLAND, THERE ARE MANY HIDDEN VALLEYS IN THE HIMALAYAS WHERE GNOMES HAVE DEVELOPED UNIQUE CULTURES AWAY FROM HUMANS. BUT MOST GNOMES IN FACT RATHER ENJOY OUR COMPANY. LIVING ON THE EDGE OF OUR LIVES SOMEHOW GIVES THEM A SENSE OF PURPOSE, THOUGH NONE WE MET COULD EVER QUITE PUT INTO WORDS WHAT THAT PURPOSE IS. POSSIBLY THEY FIND IT EMBARRASSING TO HAVE TO ADMIT THEIR DEPENDENCE ON US, WHEN IN MOST WAYS THEY ARE QUITE SELF-SUFFICIENT.

▶ THERE ARE MANY THEORIES AROUND AS TO THE ORIGIN OF CROP CIRCLES BUT THE TRUE ONE SEEMS TO HAVE ESCAPED GENERAL NOTICE SO FAR. IT IS, NATURALLY, COUNTRY-DWELLING GNOMES WHO ARE RESPONSIBLE FOR MOST OF THEM. TO GNOMES THEY ARE SIMPLY AN EXTENSION OF GARDEN DECORATION THAT HAS GOT PERHAPS A LITTLE OUT OF HAND. ALSO IT IS A BIT OF A THROWBACK TO WHEN GNOMES USED TO HELP WITH THE HARVEST, SCYTHING CORN BY MOONLIGHT. OF COURSE HUMANS DO CREATE A FEW CROP CIRCLES AS THE RESULT OF A BRIGHT MOON AND A CHEERY NIGHT DOWN THE PUB. MYSTERIOUS FORCES THAT MAY QUITE WELL BE BEAMED DOWN FROM SIRIUS REALLY DO CREATE OTHERS. BUT MOST CROP CIRCLES ARE THE WORK OF GNOMES. IT'S OBVIOUS REALLY IF YOU THINK ABOUT IT. WHO ELSE COVERS THEIR TRACKS SO WELL THAT THEY ARE INVISIBLE TO OUR EYES? WHO ELSE, APART FROM SOMEONE SHORTER THAN THE CORN ITSELF, COULD CREATE CIRCLES UNDER THE VERY EYES OF WITNESSES? GNOMES THINK CROP CIRCLES ARE THE GREATEST JOKE THEY HAVE YET PLAYED ON HUMANS. THEY HAVE BECOME AN EVERYDAY PART OF OUR LIVES BUT SO FAR ALMOST NO-ONE SUSPECTS WHO IS REALLY BEHIND THEM. NEIGHBOURING GNOME COMMUNITIES COMPETE TO MAKE THE MOST ELABORATE CROP CIRCLES, HOPING TO GET THEM INTO OUR NEWSPAPERS, WHICH IS WHY THEY ARE GETTING MORE AMBITIOUS BY THE YEAR. THIS IS ABOUT AS SERIOUS AS GNOME PRANKS EVER GET. GOBLINS ON THE OTHER HAND WILL LAUGH IF YOUR HOUSE BURNS DOWN.

ONE OF THE MOST USEFUL JOBS GNOMES DO FOR US IS TO GO AROUND WATERING ALL THE SHOOTING LITTLE PLANTS THAT WOULD OTHERWISE MISS OUT. IT IS ALSO ONE OF THE JOBS THEY FIND MOST SATISFYING BECAUSE THESE ARE THE FLOWERS THAT SPRING THE MOST SURPRISE WHEN THEY COME BURSTING THROUGH FROM BELOW.

If pressed further, they will tell you that gnomes and goblins were once very close. So close that you could not really tell them apart, except that the goblins were wilder and the tricks they played on humans were often truly vicious. Then at some point they turned their backs on each other and now live totally separate lives, ignoring each other as far as possible. Not because of hatred or any emotion as powerful as that, it is more that they just despise each other and hate anyone to think they are related.

The easiest way to deflate a goblin is to call it a garden gnome, which is worth remembering if one ever starts to plague you. They can be fierce, spiteful and vicious little creatures but the right insult easily drives them away. The most important thing is not to take them as seriously as they take themselves.

The easiest way to upset a gnome is to call it a goblin. Luckily for them, they like totally different environments so it is quite easy to avoid each other. Goblins, for instance, like nothing better than living near leaky nuclear power stations. Even when they do live in a purely natural environment they somehow manage to make it so dismal and dank that no gnome would even want to go near it.

The terms goblin and hobgoblin, incidentally, have only come to mean something bad since gnomes and dwarves went their separate ways. Originally 'hobgoblin' simply meant a helpful household sprite who enjoyed resting on the hob or hearth when all the chores were done. Most households in England and France had at least one, and they were generally considered friends.

gnomes and humans

In the past gnomes often used to share human houses, taking advantage of the shadows to come and go about their business. They would repay any kindness of their hosts by doing odd jobs around the house while they were sleeping, but the arrival of electric lighting almost entirely ended this.

Gnomes do still live in people's gardens, though, and here the old rule applies. Be kind to your gnome; leave out little gifts such as saucers of bread and milk and the odd glass of beer, and you will find many little jobs done for you. Gnomes appreciate that when sharing a garden with us most of the heavy work is done for them, so they repay this by attending to the details. They go round watering those plants that have been missed and encouraging those that feel depressed. They herd the slugs off to where they can do no damage. They nurse injured plants and do a thousand other little things that invisibly help make the garden a place of magic.

You find some gardens where at first sight everything looks perfect yet somehow there is no magic. The flowers seem regimented and there is a certain lack of sparkle to them. The garden feels no more alive than a picture in a magazine. That is because there are no gnomes at work. Probably no corners have been left free for them to set up home. Gnome gardens can be very tidy but they are also vibrant with life. You get the feeling that everything is happily growing just the way it wants to and the order is almost accidental. There is a subliminal sense of joy.

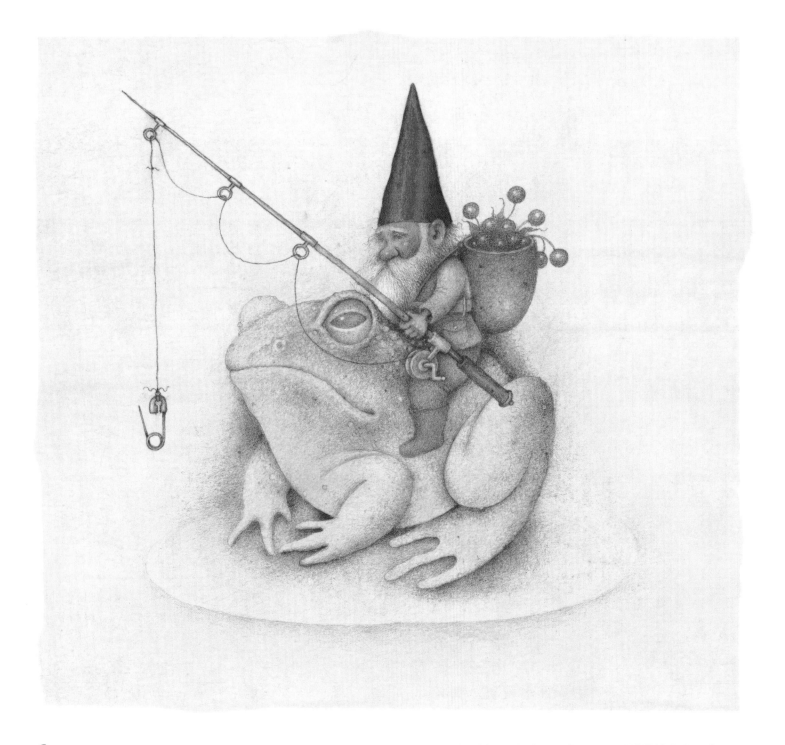

GNOMES ARE MOSTLY VEGETARIAN BUT SOME ARE PARTIAL TO EATING THE ODD FISH, SO THOSE STATUES OF THEM FISHING IN THE GARDEN POND ARE QUITE TRUE TO LIFE REALLY. AS WITH ALL FISHERMEN, HALF THE APPEAL IS SIMPLY HAVING A GOOD REASON FOR SITTING STILL FOR LONG PERIODS DOING ABSOLUTELY NOTHING BEYOND ENJOYING THE SCENERY AND MULLING OVER YOUR OWN THOUGHTS. HERE A GNOME FRIEND IS SHOWING THE WAY TO A PARTICULARLY LUCKY FISHING HOLE IN RETURN FOR SOME OF THE BAIT.

It hardly happens now, but long ago it was not unknown for large gnomes and small humans to fall in love and even marry. So lots of us carry traces of gnome blood in our veins still. It surfaces in some families and is particularly noticeable in children. Some children are practical and level-headed from the day they are born. More of them are not and need to have these qualities determinedly drummed into them. And then there are children who are particularly dreamy and defy all attempts to bring their thoughts down to earth.

We've all known at least one. They're the children who sit for hours gazing into imaginary distances, completely unaware of what's going on immediately around them. They're the ones who get excited by toadstools and really do believe they would find a crock of gold at the end of the rainbow, if only they could pinpoint where it is. These are the children who slip out at night to dance under the moon and stars. The chances are that they have a little gnome blood running through their veins. The chances are also that they will grow out of it, mostly, though some tendencies can linger into adulthood without attracting too much notice – a talent for gardening, perhaps. Or an interest in things like fairies that most people put away with their teddy bears.

One reason gnomes are fond of garden statues of themselves is that they are a useful litmus test for our attitudes towards the real thing. If we positively hate them, well, hate is a complicated emotion that is not really to be trusted. It generally implies there is something we have not come to terms with. At the least, in the case of garden gnomes, it indicates the lack of a certain kind of humour that gnomes love.

Looking down one's nose at garden gnomes, seeing them as the trivialization of a genuine and profound force of nature, is a bit more acceptable. Gnomes do not mind it so much because there is a deeper side to them after all; but it still smacks of pompousness.

At the other extreme there are some garden statues that are so twee that gnomes themselves find their sense of humour being stretched. It is a bit like what anyone feels when being hero-worshipped for the wrong reasons. It's very flattering at first but also a bit stifling if all the worshipper is interested in is one partial side. So gnomes have doubts about some garden statues themselves, but they appreciate the good intentions and often take it as a challenge to try to open the owners' eyes to the subtler aspects of gnomedom. They also appreciate the little ornamental wheelbarrows some people have in their gardens.

garden gnomes

Gnomes have a great and possibly surprising fondness for garden gnome statues, unless they are absolutely too tasteless for words. As the elvish offspring of dwarves and fairies, gnomes could be forgiven for feeling that most garden statues insult them, but almost the opposite is true – gnomes generally love them.

Occasionally if they feel humans have gone over the top they will play tricks, rearranging the statues in the middle of the night, say. Or stealing them away and planting them in the nearest woods, sending them off on journeys around the world and all that sort of thing that you hear about. But mostly gnomes take it as a compliment when we put gnome statues in our garden, especially knowing the mockery this usually inspires in the neighbours. Often they take it as an invitation to move in and the garden will then flourish, particularly if the statue is of stone because they all remember how their ancestor Glob started out as a stone statue himself.

Gnomes themselves do not remember the secret of bringing a statue truly to life, but they can do a passable imitation of it. What they are able to do is enter into a statue, soften the material from which it is made and make it dance around as they please (plaster is much easier than stone, apparently, and plastic is easier still, though some gnomes don't like the feel of it). This looks as if the statue really has just sprung to life, instead of just being operated from within like a puppet. It is a favourite trick gnomes play on humans, though they usually take care only to pick witnesses who will not be believed, such as passing drunks, madmen, artists or children.

Gnomes also appreciate garden gnome statues as a useful cover for their own activities. There is far less need to keep an ear out for approaching humans because if one does suddenly show up, all the gnome has to do is freeze and blend with the company.

THE DRAWBACK OF BICYCLES FOR GNOMES IS THE SHORTAGE OF SMOOTH PATHS FOR THEM TO USE WITHOUT CONSTANTLY RUNNING INTO HUMANS. WHERE THEY ARE LUCKY ENOUGH TO HAVE THEM, GNOME BICYCLES ARE MORE COMMON, BUT AS A MINORITY TASTE OR FORM OF ENTERTAINMENT. THEY HAVE RARELY CAUGHT ON AS A MEANS OF EVERYDAY TRANSPORT BECAUSE MOST GNOMES PREFER TO KEEP THEIR FEET FIRMLY PLANTED ON THE GROUND WHEN THEY ARE GOING ANYWHERE. GNOMES' FEET ARE TO THEM WHAT NOSES ARE TO OTHER SPECIES. THEY ARE EXTRAORDINARILY SENSITIVE TO THE CURRENTS OF THE EARTH, WHICH TELL THEM ALL KINDS OF THINGS ABOUT THEIR ENVIRONMENT THAT WE CAN ONLY GUESS AT.

gnomes and technology

Although shy of revealing themselves to us, gnomes enjoy living near humans and are fascinated by our affairs. They would never admit it, but they have in fact modelled themselves closely on us, up to a point. They've copied many of our mannerisms and ways of life, but are naturally far more conservative (in the broad sense) and there are many of our habits that they simply can't stand. Things like cars and motorways bother them less than people imagine, but they don't really approve of them and do get genuinely upset when we carve a new road through one of their preferred haunts. They are a pragmatic people though and soon settle elsewhere. There are compensations to motorways. As with railways, they eventually create ribbons of wilderness where many beleaguered wild creatures find sanctuary, despite the fumes and racket. There are many more hostile environments around.

Bicycles are the most complicated machines you are likely to find a gnome riding. Gnomes enjoy simple mechanics but few trust any machine that requires a motor more complicated than the simplest of steam engines. Gnomes do sometimes hitch long rides on human transport but only in exceptional circumstances, such as having been bitten by the travel bug and deciding to emigrate. If they want to visit distant relations they may also climb up into the back of a truck, but generally they are content to walk wherever they want to go, or ride on some friendly animal that happens to be going their way.

A few gnomes have taken to petrol- or diesel-driven lawnmowers, especially the ride-on type, and happily borrow them when humans are away, but they are rare exceptions. And all gnomes hate screaming electric mowers and scatter when one starts up. They grudgingly give these machines some credit for keeping the grass trim, but they simply can't stand the noise.

In leading their simple lives it helps that gnomes are less troubled by weather than we are, I suppose, but what they say is that they are far less bothered by the weather because they are out in it most of the time. They like a nice log fire in the winter but don't need it the way we do. It is a little luxury after being out in the snow and rain all day. In a strange way they even seem to enjoy the cold and they really love rain. When rain comes in the spring they dance around in it, making sure every seedling gets its share. It is even said they have some power to bring rain, but none of them would talk to us about this. From their reluctance we guessed that gnomes can control the weather up to a point, but didn't even want to hint at how it is done in case we guessed the secret. Which is fair enough really.

That's another thing about gnomes, they are totally honest and also polite. They prefer to avoid awkward questions rather than lying or just telling you to mind your own business. It then feels rude to keep asking again, so you don't after a while. There are many aspects of gnome life we would have loved to learn more about, but although the gnomes we questioned were open and honest about many things, they were coy about others and so we just had to let them go.

◄ A RARE PORTRAIT OF A GNOME NOT WEARING HIS HAT, JUST TO PROVE THAT THEY DO NOT IN FACT HAVE TALL, POINTY HEADS, AS SOME UNKIND RUMOURS HAVE SUGGESTED. THEIR HATS ARE HELD ON MORE BY MAGIC THAN ANY OF THE USUAL LAWS OF PHYSICS, AND THEY MEAN FAR MORE TO THEIR OWNERS THAN A MEANS OF KEEPING OFF THE RAIN...

THIS DUTCH GNOME INTRODUCED US TO THE MYSTERIES OF TULIPS, SPEAKING IN A LANGUAGE LIKE POETRY. FOR AS LONG AS HE WAS TALKING WE UNDERSTOOD PERFECTLY WHAT HE MEANT, BUT AFTERWARD IT WAS STRANGELY DIFFICULT TO CAPTURE ANY OF IT IN WORDS. ALL THAT REMAINED WAS A CERTAIN FEELING WE NOW GET EVERY TIME WE COME ACROSS A TULIP. THEY DO CARRY SOME MYSTERY WE HAVE YET TO GRASP. THERE IS A HINT OF THE HOLY GRAIL ABOUT THEM.

GNOMES LIKE SIMPLE PLEASURES AND FOR THEM THE YEARLY MIRACLE OF GROWTH AND DECAY IN A GARDEN IS ENOUGH TO KEEP THEM OCCUPIED. THEY SEE NO GREAT NEED TO EXTEND THEIR HORIZONS OR COMPLICATE THEIR LIVES UNNECESSARILY THE WAY WE DO (IN THEIR OPINION). A QUESTION MANY GNOMES ASKED US WAS 'BUT HOW IS IT THAT WITH ALL YOUR LABOUR-SAVING DEVICES YOUR LIVES SEEM TO BE MORE HECTIC AND RUSHED THAN EVER?' AND TO BE HONEST IT WAS HARD TO THINK OF A GOOD REPLY. WITHOUT ANY OF OUR ELECTRICAL GADGETS, GNOMES SEEM TO LEAD A FAR MORE COMFORTABLE AND UNHURRIED EXISTENCE THAN WE DO.

One thing we did learn is that electricity seems to be the big thing that divides humans and gnomes. They seem almost allergic to it. You will never find gnomes living near power lines or mains transformers. They say it makes them ill, which is not surprising as even humans have been known to go a bit peculiar through living under power lines. They can tolerate very low amounts of electricity but that is about all. Anything more and they say it is like hearing the continuous scrape of chalk on a dry blackboard. Even before it makes them ill, too much electricity shreds their nerves.

Also, gnomes cannot stand taking too many baths. It's one thing to be clean, they say, and quite another to go round smelling of soap all the time. Also they say washing too often ruins the skin's own natural ability to keep itself clean, so it can even make you smellier in the long run. Besides, they like the way they naturally smell and, to be fair, we only ever met one gnome who had an obvious problem with personal hygiene. So how often do they bathe? This was one of the questions they avoided, a little defensively. They know it is now common for us to shower every day, so it is certainly nothing like as often as that. Our guess was every couple of weeks or so.

GNOMES EVEN SEEM TO ENJOY THE COLD, AND THERE IS IN FACT ONE HIDING INSIDE THIS SGNOMAN WAITING TO BREAK OUT AND GIVE SOMEONE THE FRIGHT OF THEIR LIVES.

A PROLONGED SPELL OF FROZEN WEATHER DOES MAKE THEM SLUGGISH, THOUGH. THEY SPEND LONGER AND LONGER IN BED AND EVENTUALLY, LIKE OTHER HIBERNATING CREATURES, DON'T WAKE UP AT ALL TILL THE WEATHER BREAKS AND NATURE SPRINGS TO LIFE AGAIN. IN THE FROZEN NORTH, MANY GNOMES SPEND HALF THE YEAR ASLEEP THIS WAY. OTHERS HAVE EVOLVED UNDERGROUND COMMUNITIES THAT THEY RETIRE TO IN WINTER, PASSING THE TIME WITH GAMES AND GOSSIPING AND GETTING ON WITH ALL THE LITTLE JOBS THEY HAVE NO TIME FOR IN THE BRIEF SUMMER.

occupations and hobbies

GNOMES ARE FAR LESS SPECIALIZED IN THEIR OCCUPATIONS THAN HUMANS ARE. THEY HAVE A WIDE RANGE OF PRACTICAL SKILLS AND EXPECT TO DO MOST JOBS AROUND THEIR OWN HOUSES AND GARDENS THEMSELVES. THERE ARE SOME TASKS, HOWEVER, THAT ARE ONLY ENTRUSTED TO SPECIALISTS, SUCH AS SERIOUS BLACKSMITHING. MOST GNOMES ARE UP TO DOING A BIT OF TINKERING, ENOUGH TO MEND THEIR OWN POTS AND PANS, BUT FOR SERIOUS WORK SUCH AS THE FORGING OF A NEW PICK OR SHOVEL THEY WILL TURN TO A GNOME BLACKSMITH.

FORGING METALS WAS THE GREAT ART OF THE GNOMES' MALE ANCESTORS, THE DWARVES, WHO ARE SAID TO HAVE INVENTED IT FIRST. SO BLACKSMITHS ARE HELD IN SOME AWE BY OTHER GNOMES AND ARE BELIEVED TO BE THE GUARDIANS OF ANCIENT SECRETS. AND PERHAPS THEY ARE, BECAUSE TO WATCH A GNOME BLACKSMITH AT WORK IS ASTONISHING. WITH JUST A FRACTION OF THE HEAT AND EFFORT NEEDED BY HUMANS, THE METAL SEEMS ALMOST TO FLOW INTO SHAPE. THIS IMPRESSION IS STRENGTHENED BY THE SMITH MUTTERING AT HIS WORK ALL THE TIME AS IF SHAPING IT AS MUCH WITH WORDS AS THE BLOWS OF HIS HAMMER.

'it takes years of study.'

Another possibly surprising specialist profession is hatmaking. To the casual eye gnomes all seem to wear identical hats, but this is far from being the case. They nearly all wear conical hats, it is true, and most of their hats are bright red; but the exact geometry – the ratio of diameter to height – is attuned to its owner by a complex system of formulae that makes astrology seem easy. Every single facet of a gnome's build and personality gets fed into the equation.

Sometimes all these factors cancel out in such a way that two gnomes do end up with identical hats, it's true, but for completely different reasons. When this happens, they consider themselves to have gained a brother or sister. This doesn't mean they necessarily get on with them any better than with any other brothers and sisters, but it does create a special bond for which the hatmaker is ultimately held responsible. So it takes years of study for a gnome to become a recognized and trusted hatmaker. The reward is that other gnomes then hold them in almost the same awe as wizards or blacksmiths.

There is a fortunately rare condition among gnomes (particularly those who are underweight) known as Gnomostasis whereby if their heads get too cold they go into a kind of blank daze or paralysis until they warm up again. In this state they are easily mistaken for garden statues. Many a human has come across one on a walk and planted it in the garden, only to have it mysteriously disappear when the weather thaws. The wiser gnomes who suffer from this condition invest in this patented pate-warming cap with inbuilt stove, which ensures that during cold snaps they will not wake to the indignity of finding themselves dangling a fake fishing line into some goldfish pond.

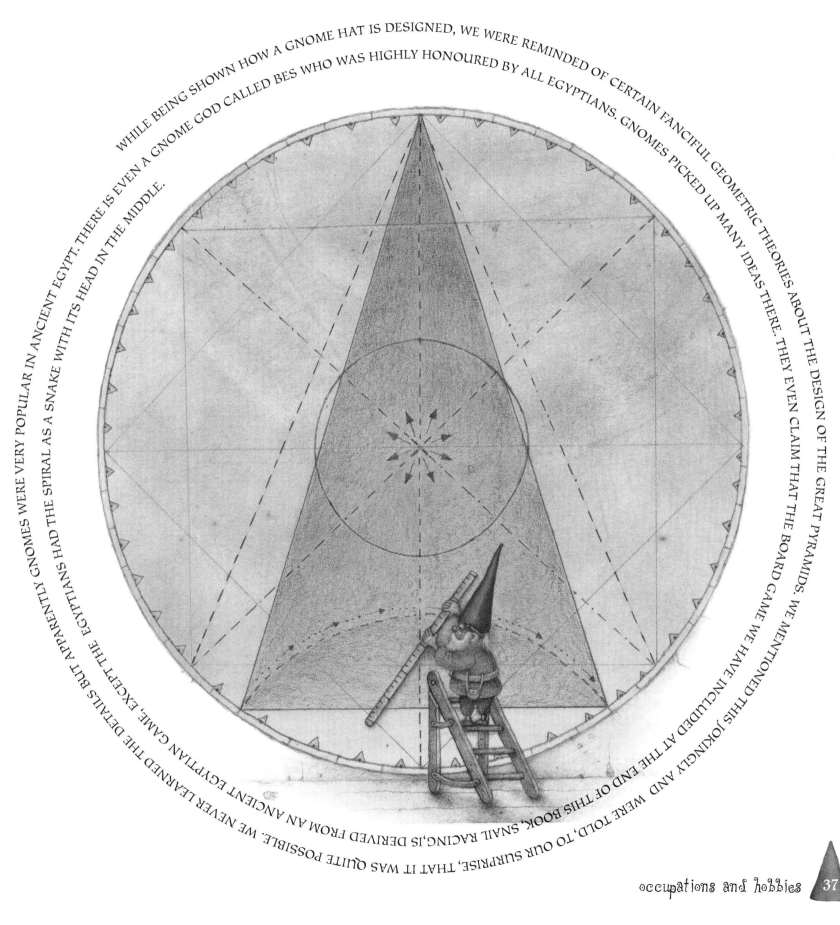

WHILE BEING SHOWN HOW A GNOME HAT IS DESIGNED, WE WERE REMINDED OF CERTAIN FANCIFUL GEOMETRIC THEORIES ABOUT THE DESIGN OF THE GREAT PYRAMIDS. WE MENTIONED THIS JOKINGLY AND WERE TOLD, TO OUR SURPRISE, THAT IT WAS QUITE POSSIBLE. WE NEVER LEARNED THE DETAILS BUT APPARENTLY GNOMES WERE VERY POPULAR IN ANCIENT EGYPT. THERE IS EVEN A GNOME GOD CALLED BES WHO WAS HIGHLY HONOURED BY ALL EGYPTIANS. GNOMES PICKED UP MANY IDEAS THERE. THEY EVEN CLAIM THAT THE BOARD GAME WE HAVE INCLUDED AT THE END OF THIS BOOK, SNAIL RACING, IS DERIVED FROM AN ANCIENT EGYPTIAN GAME, EXCEPT THE EGYPTIANS HAD THE SPIRAL AS A SNAKE WITH ITS HEAD IN THE MIDDLE.

gnome witches and wizards

Gnomes have certain powers that to us seem
magical. They can talk to plants and animals,
make themselves invisible and conjure toadstools
from the ground, but to them there is no more magic in
these things than in seeing, hearing or breathing. They just
come naturally. Making themselves invisible, for instance, they
say is half done for them because most humans simply don't
believe in them to begin with. That means they would not really want
to see a gnome even if one did step out right in front of them. From
there it only takes a small mental prod from the gnome to prompt our brains
to deny the signals from our own eyes and erase him (or her) from the scene.

It is a well-known fact that half the time we only see what we want to see anyway, so
gnomes just play upon that weakness. They use our scepticism as their cloak of
invisibility so the most any of us normally sees of a gnome is a glimpse in the corner of
our eye. When we look directly they will appear to have vanished. Gnomes cannot always rely
on this, though, because a few humans can just naturally see them anyway, which is why they
take other precautions as well.

Most gnomes are content with whatever magical (to us) talents they are born with but a few go on to study
real magic and become wizards and witches. Other gnomes always show them the greatest respect, but they
are also rather wary of them. Travelling wizards are always welcomed for the news they bring of the wider world,
for their tales and other talents; but they are also shown on their way after a visit with some relief. There is always
a danger with wizards of offending them in some obscure way and ending up with a rash of piles or boils.

Becoming a recognized gnome wizard is an arduous process involving long apprenticeship to various masters and finally a
great journey to find the designated one who will officially welcome him into the brotherhood. This quest is different in each
case because the wizard is given no clues. He just has to follow his nose and the adventures that come his way until he finds the
right Grand Master. Often it takes several human lifetimes for a gnome to earn his wizard's staff and several more to gain a reputation,
so it is not something they undertake lightly. The reward is being able to come and go as they please, always being assured of a soft bed
and supper where there is a gnome front door to knock upon.

The ambition of every gnome wizard is to have a spell of his own accepted into the Necrognomicon, the fabled grimoire, or book of spells, which apprentice
warlocks are expected to study for a third of a lifetime before they attempt any original magic. And then, to have a new spell accepted into the grimoire they
have to prove both that it is new, and that it works, before the Great Gathering of wizards, which is held only once every hundred years. The contest for a place
in the Necrognomicon is fierce and often fatal when spells backfire, but this gives the survivors something to talk about for the next hundred years.

Gnome wizard with a copy of *The Concise and Grately Abbreviated Necrognomicon*, the wizards' manual of spells for every occasion. The full edition has 23 volumes and rising, and a whole college of Swiss gnome wizards is employed in keeping it up to date and testing that the spells still work. (For unknown reasons all magic spells have a limited shelf life and from time to time, completely unpredictably, just stop working. The good thing about this is that the Necrognomicon would be even longer otherwise and completely unmanageable. The bad thing is that it can happen at just the moment when it is vitally important that the spell does work, and quickly too! There's always some down-side to magic.)

AMONG GNOMES
THE TERM 'WITCH' IS NO
MORE NEGATIVE THAN
'WIZARD'. BOTH ARE
POSSIBLY MAD, BAD AND
DANGEROUS BUT ARE MORE
LIKELY JUST TO BE
ECCENTRIC AND HARD TO
FOLLOW ONCE THEY GET
TALKING ABOUT THEIR PET
THEMES. LIKE HUMANS,
MOST GNOME WITCHES
HAVE A CAT, ALTHOUGH IT
IS GENERALLY THE WITCH
WHO SITS UPON THE CAT'S
SHOULDER.

Gnome witches have some very different ways to wizards. For a start they are not great travellers. Apart from the odd flight on a broomstick when the moon is full, they are generally home-loving folk. When they find a spot they like, they will often settle there for life, or until something like a new bypass persuades them it's time to move on. So when other gnomes need their services, they are more easily found than wizards, who just come and go unpredictably.

Also witches have little time for the Necrognomicon and use a completely different set of spells that they share by word of mouth and carry around in their heads. They are more popular than wizards, because they are more familiar, but other gnomes are still a bit wary of upsetting them and tend to visit only when it is strictly necessary.

▶ CRYSTAL BALLS ARE VERY POPULAR WITH GNOME WIZARDS, WITCHES AND FORTUNE-TELLERS. THEY USE THEM AS EASILY AS WE DO TELEVISIONS, BUT THEY HAVE THE ADVANTAGE OF BEING FULLY PORTABLE AND HAVING AN INFINITE NUMBER OF CHANNELS. PLUS, NOT ONLY CAN THEY SHOW SOMETHING HAPPENING A LONG WAY OFF, WITHOUT THE NEED FOR CAMERAS, FILM CREW OR ANY OF THAT PARAPHERNALIA, BUT ALSO THEY CAN BRING DREAMS TO LIFE WITHOUT THE DREAMER NEEDING TO BE ASLEEP. SO ANY GNOME WHO WANTS TO RECAPTURE A PARTICULARLY WONDERFUL DREAM WILL VISIT A FORTUNE-TELLER AND ASK TO BORROW THEIR CRYSTAL. GOOD CRYSTALS ARE VERY RARE, AS THEY HAVE TO BE MADE FROM NATURAL, FLAWLESS ROCK CRYSTAL THAT IS THEN GROUND AND POLISHED INTO A PERFECT SPHERE. BALLS MADE FROM MOLTEN GLASS ARE WORTHLESS EXCEPT TO GNOMES SO GIFTED WITH SECOND SIGHT THAT ALMOST ANYTHING, EVEN A DROP OF WATER ON A LEAF, WILL DO.

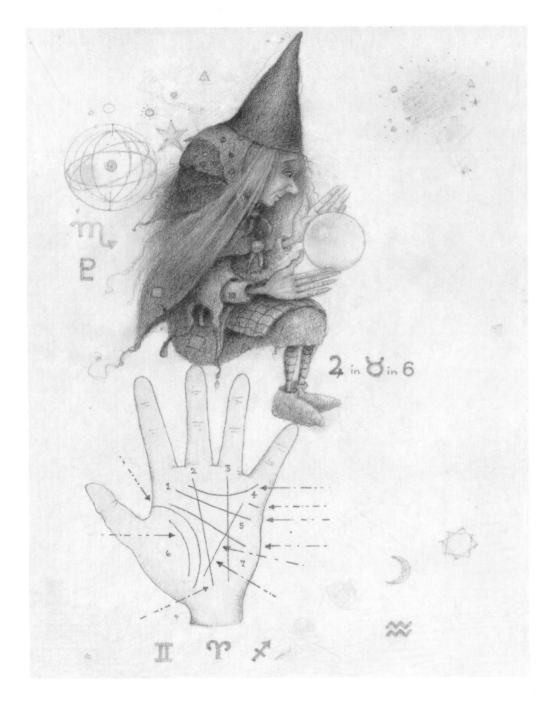

Gnomes use all the fortune-telling methods popular to humans, such as reading tealeaves, crystal gazing, palmistry, astrology and Tarot. In fact they claim to have invented many of them in the first place. They also have many methods peculiar to themselves, such as spillikins (in which a large number of straws are tossed into a random pile and then somehow 'read') and reading spiderwebs. Gnome fortune-tellers are not respected as much as wizards or witches, who consider them amateurs, but are generally more popular because they are considered totally harmless.

gnome behaviour

Apart from wizards, hermits and a few other eccentrics, gnomes are sociable and live settled domestic lives near others of their own kind. But every now and then one of them will take to wandering off alone and eventually disappear for tens of years at a time. This gnomadic behaviour is not really approved of by the rest, but it is accepted as a strange affliction that could strike any of them, so they are sympathetic. 'Bitten by the travel bug' they will tell, shaking their heads sadly.

And in fact they seriously do believe that there is such a bug, very rare but as real to them as any horsefly, midge or mosquito. If wanderers ever return (and many do not), their old friends and neighbours give them a cautiously warm welcome (cautious in case the mania has still not quite worn off) and help them set up home again. They have little patience with travellers' tales, though. For their penance the wanderers are generally obliged to listen patiently to blow-by-blow accounts of every little thing that has happened at home while they were away. Only then maybe are they asked to say a little of their own adventures, if they can still remember them.

GNOME FORTUNE-TELLERS ARE SELF-TRAINED AND ARE USUALLY CHATTY, CHEERY INDIVIDUALS. WITCHES AND WIZARDS LOOK DOWN ON THEM BUT THEY ARE OFTEN JUST AS SKILLED, OR EVEN MORE SO. THEY SIMPLY CAN'T BE BOTHERED WITH GOING THROUGH THE LONG APPRENTICESHIP REQUIRED FOR FORMAL RECOGNITION AND THIS SEEMS TO MAKE THEM NICER, MORE APPROACHABLE INDIVIDUALS. THEY TEND TO BE CONSIDERED HARMLESS BUT OCCASIONALLY HELPFUL ECCENTRICS BY OTHER GNOMES. VERY ENTERTAINING COMPANY, ESPECIALLY AT FAIRS, BUT NOTHING TO BE AFRAID OF.

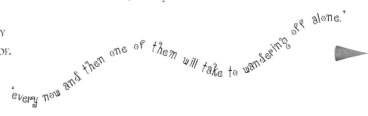

'every now and then one of them will take to wandering off alone.'

MANY GNOMES TAKE UP ASTRONOMY AS A HOBBY. OR ASTROLOGY, IF YOU PREFER; THEY SEE NO GREAT DIFFERENCE THEMSELVES. UNTIL RECENTLY THEY WERE STREETS AHEAD OF US TOO, BECAUSE WITH THEIR SHARP EYES EVEN A SIMPLE TELESCOPE SHOWS THEM SWARMS OF STARS THAT WERE INVISIBLE TO US BEFORE WE FIRED SATELLITES INTO SPACE. IN THE PAST THEIR THEORIES WERE ALSO WAY IN ADVANCE OF OURS. IT WAS GNOMES WHO TOLD THE ANCIENT GREEKS ABOUT THE WORLD BEING ROUND AND SOME EVEN BELIEVED THEM, THOUGH MOST THOUGHT THE IDEA TOO FAR-FETCHED. GNOMES (ALTHOUGH STRICTLY SPEAKING IT WAS DWARVES, ACCORDING TO THE TERMS WE ARE USING) ALSO TAUGHT THE ANCIENT GREEKS A LOT OF OTHER THINGS AND EVEN STARTED A WHOLE NEW SCHOOL OF POETRY BASED ON THEIR OWN RIDDLES.

MUCH OF IT REMAINS DEFIANTLY INCOMPREHENSIBLE TO THIS DAY AND IS RESPONSIBLE FOR THE PHRASE 'GNOMIC UTTERANCE', MEANING SOMETHING THAT SOUNDS AS IF IT WOULD BE INCREDIBLY MEANINGFUL IF ONLY WE UNDERSTOOD IT. IN ASTRONOMY, HOWEVER, GNOMES APPEAR TO HAVE FALLEN BEHIND OF LATE. MENTION BLACK HOLES AND WHITE DWARFS AND THEY JUST SMILE INDULGENTLY AND CHANGE THE SUBJECT. WE'RE PRETTY SURE THEY'RE JUST PRETENDING TO KNOW BETTER, BUT WITH GNOMES IT NEVER PAYS TO BE TOO SMUG.

HAVING NO POLICE, GNOMES SORT OUT THEIR OWN JUSTICE. IT'S RARE THAT ANY OF THEM UPSETS THE OTHERS ENOUGH TO BE LOCKED IN STOCKS LIKE THIS FOR REAL, THOUGH. USUALLY THIS IS ONLY A PRANK THAT GETS PLAYED ON TIPSY GNOMES WHO'VE HAD A DROP TOO MUCH DANDELION WINE.

Gnomes are less attached to treasure than, say, leprechauns, but they do have a certain love of gold, silver and jewels. The attitude varies between males and females. Female gnomes love jewellery as pretty decoration. They will wear a necklace for a while and then just give it away when they find a new one they like better. Males are far more possessive, even competitive, in the way they hoard treasure. They like to go hunting for it, usually in groups of up to a dozen. The only trouble with finding treasure, though, is that their wives usually invite all their friends round to take their pick of it. So when they find treasure, the males quickly feel obliged to go off and bury it again somewhere else.

The only trouble with this is that there is always the danger of some total stranger coming along and running off with it. This is fair enough in a way. The law of 'Finders Keepers, Losers Weepers' applies to gnome treasure as much as any other. But of course this doesn't stop gnomes getting very irate when it happens to them. So burying treasure is always a solitary activity and carried out according to very complicated directions for finding it again.

The only trouble with this is remembering the directions. Sometimes gnomes write them out and bury the directions too, but this can get out of hand. The wiser gnomes keep treasure hunting as just an occasional hobby.

◀ MALE GNOMES' LOVE OF TREASURE IS A MARK OF THEIR DWARFISH ORIGIN, MUCH AS WE HAVE AN APPENDIX. IT IS ALMOST COMPLETELY IRRELEVANT TO MOST OF THEIR EVERYDAY ACTIVITIES AND INTERESTS, BUT IT IS AN ITCH THEY HAVE TO SCRATCH FROM TIME TO TIME JUST TO FEEL LIKE THEMSELVES AGAIN.

GNOMES DO NOT OF COURSE NEED A COMPASS TO TELL THEM WHICH WAY IS NORTH, SOUTH, EAST OR WEST. IT IS SOMETHING THEY ARE AS CONSTANTLY AWARE OF AS WE ARE OF THE TIME OF DAY. MORE SO POSSIBLY, BUT THEY LIKE OUR PARAPHERNALIA OF WEATHERCOCKS AND COMPASSES. YOU CAN NEVER TRUST THE COMPASS SIGNS ON A GNOME TREASURE MAP, THOUGH, BECAUSE THEY WILL HAVE DECIDED BEFOREHAND THAT THE INDICATED N WILL REALLY BE SSW OR SOMETHING LIKE THAT.

There are many differences between male and female gnomes. Female gnomes get mentioned so rarely that some people believe there aren't any, but in fact their numbers are just about even and gnomes tend to live as married couples. The females are a bit more stay-at-home than the males, but that is not why they seem less common. They simply have far more acute senses than the males and are usually long gone by the time you or I blunder along.

Female gnomes have other differences too, which show they have more of the fairy in them than the males. When the males go digging for treasure, they go hunting instead for rare herbs and flowers. And on these excursions they are always delighted to run into other gnomes or fairies, while the treasure hunters do all they can to avoid them. There is nothing more embarrassed than two parties of gnome treasure hunters accidentally bumping into each other and pretending they are just out for a spot of midnight gardening.

GNOMES CAN SEE BETTER THAN CATS IN THE DARK, BUT THEY NEED CANDLES AND OIL LAMPS IF THEY WANT TO READ OR KNIT OR ANYTHING LIKE THAT. ALSO THEY OFTEN LIGHT CANDLES SIMPLY TO ENJOY THEIR ROSY GLOW, MUCH AS WE LIGHT OPEN FIRES EVEN THOUGH WE HAVE CENTRAL HEATING. THERE IS A SPECIAL CHARM TO FACES AND PLACES SEEN ONLY IN THE HALF-LIGHT THAT HELPS US APPRECIATE THEIR CHARMS AFRESH.

ROSES ARE LOVE TOKENS FOR GNOMES. THE SUREST SIGN THAT ONE GNOME FANCIES ANOTHER IS THE GIFT OF A ROSE. OFTEN IT IS DONE IN A SEEMINGLY ACCIDENTAL WAY, SO THE RECIPIENT CANNOT BE QUITE SURE THAT ANYTHING IS INTENDED. OFTEN THERE IS GREAT EMBARRASSMENT WHEN IT REALLY IS A TOTALLY INNOCENT GIFT. BUT USUALLY THE PRESENT OF A ROSE IS ACCOMPANIED BY A LONG, MEANINGFUL LOOK, AS HERE. YOU'D HAVE TO BE BLIND NOT TO KNOW IT'S A COME-ON.

gnome economics

Gnomes rarely use money (apart from the Zurich variety) and get by purely by barter in the little trading that they do. As most of them grow or simply pick their own food, collect their own firewood and are handy with almost any kind of tool, there is little need of trade. This means that when it does arise there is no fixed exchange rate for anything, it depends purely on the circumstances and need of the parties involved.

When they trade, gnomes simply haggle till some compromise is reached, which can take days, weeks, months or even years. Often they resort to the wildest insults and even blows. Both parties will swear they are being robbed blind, there will be tears and much storming off in rage; but you can tell the fairness of an exchange by the size of the grin on each face as they walk away at the end. It's rare that either gnome is genuinely disappointed, as bargaining is one of their preferred sports and they drag it out just to make the most of it.

most collect their own firewood.

gnome sports and pastimes

Gnomes are an industrious seeming people but they do not work all the time. Far from it in fact; they set very sensible limits to work and play. Even when they are working, they choose a steady pace that allows time enough to enjoy what they're doing, while they are doing it. To them work is rarely just a means to an end, they enjoy it in itself. The idea of working flat out to meet a deadline is quite alien to gnomes. They can do it in emergencies but otherwise they prefer just to take whatever time seems natural to get a job done properly.

'Time enough' is one of the most common gnome sayings, followed by 'how long is a piece of string?' (when you ask them how long a job is likely to take). And generally speaking this attitude seems to serve their purposes well enough. It is very rare to find a gnome looking stressed or hurried or even worried for that matter. They watch us rushing around with great amusement and put it all down to the self-imposed tyranny of clocks. They often have clocks in their homes but simply don't pay them much attention. They just enjoy the gentle ticking, which is always about half the pace of ours. The only clock they do pay much attention to is that of the sun and they mark the changing seasons with regular festivals of singing and dancing and every kind of party entertainment imaginable.

PERHAPS IT IS BECAUSE GNOMES LIVE SO MUCH LONGER THAN WE DO THAT THEY CAN AFFORD TO TAKE LIFE AT SUCH A RELAXED PACE. BUT THERE SEEMS MORE TO IT THAN THAT. GNOMES ARE FAR SUBTLER THINKERS THAN THEY LET ON. THEIR VIEW IS THAT IF YOU HAVE TO EXPLAIN AN IDEA AT GREAT LENGTH, THE CHANCES ARE YOU HAVEN'T REALLY WORKED IT OUT PROPERLY YET. IT'S LIKE TRYING TO EXPLAIN WHY A JOKE IS FUNNY WHEN IT EITHER IS OR ISN'T. SO WHEN IT COMES TO THEIR USE OF TIME, GNOMES DO HAVE A LONG LIFE TO THANK FOR SOME OF IT, BUT THEY ALSO ORGANIZE THEIR DAY-TO-DAY EXISTENCE FAR BETTER. THEY HAVE A MUCH MORE REALISTIC IDEA OF HOW LONG THINGS ARE GOING TO TAKE AND LIMIT THEIR EXPECTATIONS ACCORDINGLY.

Gnomes enjoy any kind of race but they take sports much less seriously than we do. There is no such thing as a professional gnome athlete for instance, the idea is totally alien to them. Their idea of training for a race is a quick limber up just beforehand. Snail racing is very popular but it is an acquired taste, we felt, a bit like watching English village cricket. Most of the time nothing very much happens at all, and when it does you have usually just nodded off.

▶ SNOW SLEDGING IN SLIPPERY SNAIL SHELLS (TRY SAYING IT QUICKLY AFTER A FEW BEERS!). HERE WE SEE SNAIL SHELLS BEING MADE TO TRAVEL FASTER THAN THEIR ORIGINAL OWNERS WOULD EVER HAVE DREAMED POSSIBLE, HELPED BY BEING HIGHLY POLISHED WITH LINSEED OIL. GNOMES SEE NOTHING GHOULISH IN EMPLOYING THE REMAINS OF OLD SNAIL FRIENDS IN THIS WAY, THOUGH THEY DO LEAVE THE SHELLS TO WEATHER FOR A WINTER OR SO BEFORE THINKING OF A USE FOR THEM.

gnome entertainment

People imagine that as very few gnome families have radio, television or telephones, they must spend their evenings in scintillating conversation. This can happen, but usually only when they have visitors. After the day's gossip has been aired over dinner, most gnome families settle down to reading, sewing, knitting and playing cards or other games. On warm summer nights they do this out in the open but in winter they gather in each other's houses around a fire. Gnomes do have a few inns and other public houses, but more often they prefer just to visit each other during winter and meet in the open during summer.

One of the gnomes' preferred games is wordplay. They are famous for their riddles and will often spend hours trying to solve them before giving up and begging for the answer. In fact we found that normal conversation with a gnome is a bit like an ongoing riddle anyway, because there is usually a second meaning behind anything they say. On the next page are a few gnome riddles we managed to gather from them:

▶ GNOME CARDS ARE THE SAME AS OURS EXCEPT THAT THE SUITS ARE HEARTS, DIAMONDS, CLOVER AND GARDEN SPADES. THE WILD CARDS ARE OF COURSE FOUR LEAFED CLOVERS.

◀ ALTHOUGH THEY RARELY USE THEM FOR LONG DISTANCES, GNOMES HAVE MANY EXOTIC FORMS OF TRANSPORT THAT THEY ENJOY RACING DOWNHILL, SUCH AS THIS SHELL TRICYCLE WHICH BEAT ALL-COMERS IN THE GNOME MIDSUMMER FAIR IN WILTSHIRE, WHICH WE WERE LUCKY ENOUGH TO ATTEND.

1. I have fed upon books, but know not a letter,
   I have lived in a library but am none the wiser.
   I have devoured the poets
   But you would not know it.
   Who am I?

2. Where is happiness always to be found?

3. What fish has its eyes closest together?

4. What sweetens the cup of life
   But if it loses one letter
   Makes it bitter?

5. Built long ago, yet made today,
   Used most when most are asleep:
   Few would wish to give me away,
   But only the idle wish me to keep.
   What am I?

6. Who spends the day fighting to stay apart
   And the night sleeping together?

7. I went to the wood and got it.
   When I had it I looked for it.
   When I could not find it
   I brought it home in my hand.
   What is it?

answers on page 93

GNOMES ARE FOND OF HEARING BOOKS READ ALOUD BECAUSE IT FREES THEIR EYES AND HANDS FOR OTHER THINGS, IF THEY SO WISH. IT IS UNCOMMON FOR THEM TO DRAG THEIR OWN FURNITURE OUTSIDE LIKE THIS, THOUGH, BECAUSE FOR HALF THE YEAR THEY CAN SIMPLY COAX UP TOADSTOOLS FROM THE GROUND TO SIT ON, BUT THIS GNOME COUPLE HAS PLAINLY GOT ATTACHED TO THEIR HOME COMFORTS.

the Gnoma sutra

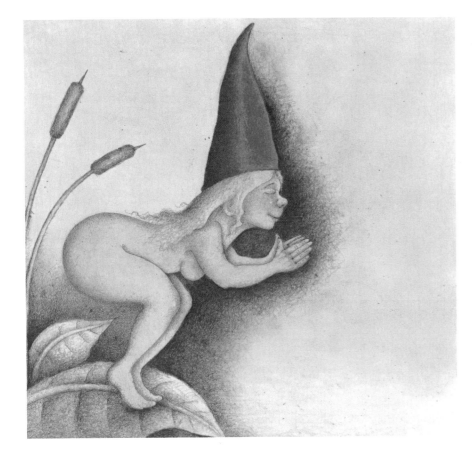

Gnomes are generally rather prudish about taking off their clothes; very prudish in fact. They only ever undress completely when taking a bath and even then they cover all the mirrors. But occasionally some of the younger ones will rebel and throw away both clothes and inhibitions to go skinny-dipping and dancing naked in the moonlight. This seems to happen most often after they have been experimenting with mushrooms, but this may be coincidence. Such outbreaks of liberation are generally short-lived though, and they get terribly embarrassed afterwards. Most gnomes have a famous lack of interest in sex. Often they forget all about it for years on end and only remember when some friend surreptitiously slips them a copy of the fabled gnome sex manual, the Gnoma Sutra.

In our researches we kept hearing whispered talk of this fabulous treasure, which we were assured is largely responsible for the continuing existence of the gnome race. It has never yet been seen by human eyes, we were assured. After much perseverance we hoped to be able to show a few pages from it here, but sadly at the last moment our promised copy did not materialize. Almost certainly our friend got cold feet and was afraid of exposing gnomes to ridicule.

Gnome homes

GNOMES HAVE GREAT IMAGINATION AS BUILDERS LEFT UNTOUCHED BY HUMANS, EVEN IN CITIES. BEHIND GARDEN SHEDS CAT OR MOUSE WILL NOTICE.

AND MAKE USE OF ANY MATERIAL THAT COMES TO HAND. OFTEN AND FACTORY WALLS AND TANGLED BANKS OF BRAMBLE, THERE'S

WILL NOTICE; BUT IT IS SURPRISING HOW MANY ODD CORNERS ARE AND EVEN MANSIONS, AND NONE BUT THE ODD PASSING

MANY AN ODD CORNER WHERE GNOMES CAN BUILD THEIR HOUSES THEY HAVE TO DISGUISE THEIR HOMES OF COURSE, SO NO HUMAN PASSERS-BY

As a broad rule of thumb, the size of a gnome's home is a measure of how many other gnomes live nearby, because they take turns to pitch in and help build each other's houses on a voluntary basis. The hosts just provide a barrel of beer and an endless supply of pies and the house takes shape around them. The owners do get some say as to what kind of house they want. At least, the others generally listen politely as they outline their vision, but this is often little more than a formality because they then tend to go ahead and do whatever they think is needed. This accounts for the often rather eccentric look of gnome dwellings and why they usually have at least one room with no doors or windows.

CITY-DWELLING GNOMES ARE STILL ATTRACTED TO GARDENS AND THE ODD POCKETS OF WASTELAND THAT SURVIVE IN EVEN THE DENSEST OF CITIES, BUT SOME TAKE WHOLEHEARTEDLY TO CITY LIFE, GIVE UP GARDENING AND LIVE LARGELY BY TRADING USEFUL ODDS AND ENDS WITH THEIR MORE BUCOLIC COUSINS. THE MOST ENTERPRISING MAKE REGULAR TRIPS FAR INTO THE COUNTRY AND TRADE THEIR TRINKETS FOR RARE HERBS AND TOADSTOOLS UNOBTAINABLE IN THE CITY. YOU'D BE AMAZED WHAT USES GNOMES FIND FOR THE ODDS AND ENDS WE THROW AWAY. SILVER THIMBLES HAVE BEEN KNOWN TO SERVE AS GNOME GOBLETS FOR A CENTURY OR TWO.

HERE WE SEE A GROUP OF GNOMES HARD AT WORK ON A FRIEND'S HOUSE, STARTING FROM SCRATCH WITH RAW MATERIALS THEY HAPPEN TO HAVE FOUND LYING AROUND NEARBY. GNOME HOUSES ARE RARELY THIS OBVIOUS BUT THESE GNOMES LIVE IN A PARTICULARLY ISOLATED SPOT SURROUNDED BY BOGS, SO THEY FEEL FREER THAN MOST TO EXPRESS THEMSELVES ARCHITECTURALLY.

gnome alone

Gnomes can turn almost anything they fancy into a home, including, as you see on the right, dustbins. We got to know this gnome rather well. At first we thought he was a hermit by choice, living so far from the others. We were surprised by his eager welcome, though, and he was remarkably chatty for a hermit. Then it turned out he had no sense of smell and had not thought to clean out his dustbin before converting it.

At least, it's not that he had no sense of smell, just a very peculiar one. He actually seemed to enjoy the stench in which he lived. When he got on to talking about how rarely he had visitors, we didn't have the heart to suggest that maybe it was because he and his house smelt worse than a cesspool. But to us it was a small price to pay for finding such a talkative informant; and for every tale of woe that we had to sit through (and there were a good few of these – this was not a happy gnome) there was a corresponding gem of gnome lore.

In fact, to be honest, we probably owe half this book to the little fellow, one way or another. Which only goes to prove what the old alchemists used to say – that the brightest treasures are often found in the muckiest places.

AS EVERYONE KNOWS, IN ANCIENT TIMES SOME NYMPH OR GODDESS GUARDED EVERY SPRING AND WELL. LATER THE SAINTS TOOK OVER AND WHEN THEY LOST INTEREST SOME OF THE OLD FAIRIES RETURNED. BUT THESE DAYS IT IS MOSTLY GNOMES WHO TEND MAGIC WELLS. THEY STILL HAVE THE POWER TO GRANT BLESSINGS OF LUCK TO THOSE WHO TOSS COINS INTO THEM, THOUGH THESE DAYS THEY ARE UNLIKELY TO POP OUT IN PERSON AND OFFER TO GRANT THREE WISHES. THAT WAS MOSTLY A RUMOUR ANYWAY. IT DID HAPPEN FROM TIME TO TIME BUT THERE WAS ALWAYS MORE TO THE STORY THAN JUST THE TOSSING IN OF A COIN.

GNOMES ARE GREAT READERS AND ANY GNOME WITH A GOOD LIBRARY IS NEVER SHORT OF VISITORS. HERE WE SEE THE WIFE OF THE HOUSE ENTERTAINING GUESTS WHILE HER HUSBAND SNORES IN BED UPSTAIRS. SHE DOESN'T SEEM TO MIND SO HE MUST BE TIRED OUT THROUGH HAVING DONE SOMETHING TO PLEASE HER. HOLLOW TREES ARE A FAVOURITE CHOICE FOR GNOME HOMES, FOR REASONS THAT ARE OBVIOUS – READY-MADE STRUCTURE AND NATURAL DISGUISE. HOLLOW TREES ARE POPULAR WITH OTHER CREATURES TOO, THOUGH, SO THERE ARE NEVER ENOUGH TO GO AROUND. GNOMES HAVE BEEN KNOWN TO HOLLOW OUT TREES FOR THEMSELVES, BUT IT IS VERY HARD LABOUR FOR WHICH THEY FIND FEWER VOLUNTEERS THAN FOR OTHER KINDS OF HOME.

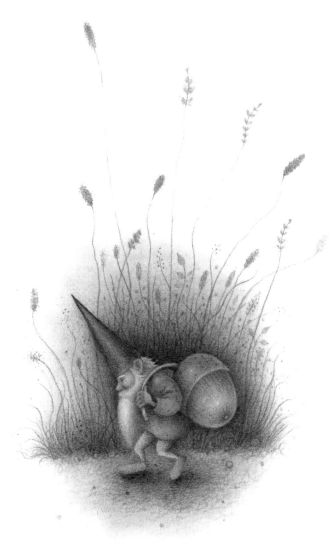

CONDOMINIUM BEHIND THE POTTING SHED. GNOMES GENERALLY DO NOT LIVE QUITE AS CLOSE TOGETHER AS THIS BUT THEY WILL TRY ANYTHING AND THIS PILE OF CLAY FLOWERPOTS JUST LENT ITSELF NATURALLY TO BEING TURNED INTO A BLOCK OF HIGH-RISE FLATS. ONE OF THE FEW CONCESSIONS GNOMES MAKE TO OUR PLASTICS INDUSTRY IS THAT THEY GRUDGINGLY ADMIT THAT PLASTIC FLOWERPOTS ARE BETTER FOR MOST PLANTS THAN THE OLD CLAY ONES. IT'S SAD BUT TRUE THAT THE LOOK AND FEEL OF THE POTS DOES NOT COME INTO IT. PLASTIC JUST RETAINS THE MOISTURE BETTER. ALTHOUGH THEY HATE THE LOOK OF THEM, GNOMES EVEN USE PLASTIC FLOWERPOTS THEMSELVES, BUT THEY ARE A BIT EMBARRASSED ABOUT IT AND TEND TO HIDE THEM BEHIND THE OTHERS.

OAKS ARE THE GNOMES' PREFERRED TREES AND THEY DELIGHT IN PLANTING NEW ONES FOR FUTURE GENERATIONS, OFTEN CARRYING AN ACORN MILES TO THE RIGHT SPOT AND CAREFULLY TENDING THE YOUNG TREE TILL IT IS TALL AND STRONG ENOUGH TO FEND FOR ITSELF. THE OAK IS THE KING OF ALL TREES, THEY WILL TELL YOU, BECAUSE IT IS HOME TO MORE CREATURES THAN ANY OTHER. IT IS ALSO THE MOST COMMON HOST OF MISTLETOE, WHICH THE GNOMES USE FOR A NUMBER OF POTENT ELIXIRS AND MEDICINES. IN HUMANS MISTLETOE (IN THE RIGHT MEASURE) IS A VALUABLE REMEDY FOR NERVOUSNESS AND STRESS, BUT GNOMES DON'T SUFFER MUCH FROM EITHER AND GENERALLY USE IT JUST TO CHEER THEMSELVES UP EVEN MORE. THEY ALSO SAY IT KEEPS THEM IMMUNE FROM MANY OF THE ILLNESSES THAT AFFLICT US, AND THERE MUST BE SOMETHING IN THIS BECAUSE IT IS RARE TO FIND A GNOME WHO IS NOT IN THE BEST OF HEALTH.

gnome decoration

Gnomes have much the same tastes as humans in furnishing and decoration of their houses, though as in other things they tend to be simpler, more old-fashioned and much less fussy than us. The general look of their houses inside is pretty much what one might have expected in a country cottage some hundred or more years ago, and even those with grander ideas tend not to carry them all the way through. Compared with our standards of decoration today, it looks as if gnomes are only playing at it. On the other hand they say we take decorating far too seriously and are only half as happy with our homes for ten times the effort.

Gnomes like to hang pictures on their walls and in this respect they are far choosier than us. They don't give a thought to whether a painting will match the general décor (if there is much to match). They only care for the picture itself, whether it means anything to them. The general standard of art in their homes is far higher than ours and they have a lively appreciation of human art as well as their own. Damien Hurst is still a bit beyond them but abstract art and surrealism are surprisingly popular. Among older artists Bruegel, William Blake and van Gogh are also great favourites.

They also have many great painters themselves, some of whose work is even known to us. They are classed as 'miniatures', though, and everyone marvels at how some unsung human artist managed to paint so tiny an image. 'They must have used a single hair of sable' we say to each other, little guessing the truth. Most great gnome painters are totally unknown to us, however, but we did manage to track down one and persuaded him to pose with one of his masterpieces.

Gnomes do not generally plan their interior decoration in any grand overall way. Their homes simply take shape around them according to need, starting from a bare space in which they plonk themselves down with whatever possessions they have brought from their last home. They have less of a fixed idea in advance than we do of how a house should be arranged, and never read glossy furnishing magazines. They do not decorate to impress, so their homes are very personal. You can immediately tell what their tastes and interests are.

PETE GNOMDRIAN, ONE OF THE FOREMOST EXPONENTS OF GNOMIC ABSTRACT ART IN THE WORLD, WITH HIS FOUR SLICES OF TOMATO XXIII, GENERALLY ACKNOWLEDGED AS THE BOLDEST VISUAL STATEMENT FROM HIS ACCLAIMED RED PERIOD. CROWDS OF GNOMES FAINTED AT ITS FIRST SHOWING IN AMSTERDAM, AND THEN RUSHED OUT TO EAT ALL THE TOMATOES THEY COULD LAY THEIR HANDS ON.

IN HIDDEN VALLEYS OF THE SWISS ALPS, AS YET UNDISCOVERED BY PRYING HUMAN EYES, SOME GNOMES HAVE WITHDRAWN FROM ALL ASSOCIATION WITH US AND DEVELOPED A UNIQUE CULTURE UNTROUBLED BY THE OUTSIDE WORLD. HERE ONE FINDS THEIR GRANDEST ARCHITECTURAL PROJECTS, SUCH AS CASTLES LIKE THIS. SWITZERLAND IS OFTEN THE DESTINATION OF EUROPEAN GNOMES WHO GET SERIOUSLY BITTEN BY THE TRAVEL BUG. THEY GO TO SEE FOR THEMSELVES IF THE LEGENDS ARE TRUE. OF COURSE HALF OF WHAT THEY SAY IS NOT BELIEVED, IF AND WHEN THEY EVER COME HOME AGAIN. OTHER GNOMES JUST THINK THEY ARE EXAGGERATING, BUT IF HALF THE TALES ARE TRUE, THE HIDDEN GNOMES OF SWITZERLAND ARE AN INDUSTRIOUS BUNCH.

THROUGH THE BRIGHT, MILD SUMMER THEY BUSILY TEND THEIR GARDENS AND LARGE HERDS OF CHAMOIS DEER, FROM WHOSE MILK THEY MAKE A DISTINCTIVE CHEESE THAT HELPS KEEP THEM GOING THROUGH THE WINTER. DURING THE BLIZZARDS OF WINTER THEY BUSILY PLAN NEW WINGS TO THEIR PALACES AND RUSH OUT TO ADD EXTENSIONS WHENEVER THE WEATHER LIFTS. THIS IS WHERE THE HIGHEST GNOME WIZARDS AND WITCHES GO FOR MUCH OF THEIR LONG APPRENTICESHIP. THIS IS ALSO WHERE, IF ANYWHERE, ONE COULD PROBABLY HEAR THE TRUEST AND MOST ANCIENT LEGENDS OF THE GNOMES' ORIGINS TODAY. SADLY WE WERE QUITE UNABLE TO LEARN CLEAR ENOUGH DIRECTIONS TO MAKE THE JOURNEY.

gnome cooking

Gnomes are the most wonderful cooks in the world and use a wide range of foods that have almost been forgotten by humans. Wild mushrooms and toadstools are probably the most popular ingredients of their cooking. They have an understanding of their properties that would astonish any human mycologist. But we have not included any mushroom recipes in this book for the simple reason that many of the varieties they eat are deadly poisonous to us, such as the *Amanita Muscaria* (or Fly Agaric). This is the famous red-capped, white-spotted toadstool particularly associated with gnomes and other fairy folk. It is one of their favourite dishes and when it is in season they always lay in dried stock to last the rest of the year.

Some mushrooms are poisonous even to them if not carefully blended in the right proportion with other ingredients. The history of gnome cooking is littered with the sad tombs of brave gastrognomic adventurers who sampled the wrong mix of toadstools. Altogether it is far too dangerous a subject for amateurs like us to venture into. The only mushrooms we recommend are those on the shelf of your supermarket.

Gnomes also use many of what we call weeds in their cooking. It is a relic of their country origins. They even cultivate them up to a point in out-of-the-way corners of our gardens. They also trade domesticated vegetables like lettuces and carrots with their country cousins for things like blackberries and Ink Cap toadstools, which are harder for them to grow in the suburbs.

THE PATENTED GOBLIN TEASMADE, GUARANTEED TO WAKE THE HOUSEHOLD WITH A REFRESHING BREW. ADMITTEDLY, SINCE SOMEONE HAS TO BE UP ANYWAY TO OPERATE IT, IT WOULD PROBABLY BE EASIER FOR HIM JUST TO BOIL A KETTLE AND CLANG THE BELL BY HAND, BUT NO ONE HAD THE HEART TO POINT THIS OUT TO THE INVENTOR. MANY GNOME INVENTIONS SEEM TO WORK LIKE THIS. INGENIOUS THOUGH THEY ARE IN MANY WAYS, THEY ACTUALLY MAKE THE TASK LONGER AND MORE COMPLICATED THAN IT WAS IN THE FIRST PLACE. PERHAPS THAT IS WHY TECHNOLOGY HAS NEVER REALLY CAUGHT ON WITH GNOMES. IT IS JUST THE ECCENTRICS WHO LIKE TO TINKER WITH MACHINES.

THIS PARTICULAR TEASMADE WAS LATER MODIFIED INTO THE VERY FIRST GNOME-MADE STEAM TRACTOR AND THE BELL CAME IN VERY USEFUL FOR WARNING PEOPLE TO GET OUT OF THE WAY. THE ORIGINAL IDEA, HOWEVER, WAS FAMOUSLY ADAPTED BY HUMANS FOR A TEA-MAKING ELECTRICAL ALARM CLOCK THAT SOLD MILLIONS DURING ITS HEYDAY. BEYOND THE NAME, NO CREDIT WAS OF COURSE GIVEN TO GNOMES, BUT THEY ARE USED TO THAT.

On the next page we see two gnomes who have just got married, picking mushrooms for their honeymoon. This lasts a whole month and is spent in some secret place they have prepared in advance. They see none of their family and friends during this time, but use it to decide where to live. More than this, gnomes usually decline to say. One guesses that a honeymoon for them is much the same as with us, only less rushed. One couple shyly showed us their honeymoon place, a makeshift bower near a waterfall, and went all dewy-eyed at the recollection. Some gnomes even stay on and make their homes where they honeymoon, but usually the place is too remote for them to enjoy long.

The dark before dawn is reckoned to be the best time for picking mushrooms because that is when their energy is most concentrated in the heads. Gnomes can also more or less conjure up mushrooms at will. They just whisper to the dormant plant below ground and toadstools just spring up before your very eyes. Gnomes claim there is no magic in this, they simply prompt the plant to do what it was about to do anyway; but we couldn't manage it, so some kind of supernatural power surely is involved. It is a very handy talent, though, because it saves gnomes having to take tables and chairs with them on a picnic.

GNOMES OFTEN HELP THEMSELVES TO OUR COOKING IMPLEMENTS WHEN WE HAVE
FINISHED WITH THEM BECAUSE IT SAVES THEM NO END OF TROUBLE IN MAKING THEIR
OWN. THEY WILL EVEN OCCASIONALLY SNEAK INTO OUR KITCHENS AT NIGHT TO BORROW THE
ONES WE STILL USE, THOUGH ONLY WHEN THEY HAVE SOME REAL COOKING EMERGENCY ON
THEIR HANDS, SUCH AS A WEDDING OR THE UNANNOUNCED ARRIVAL OF ALL THEIR RELATIONS.

BEING ALLERGIC TO ELECTRICITY, GNOMES HAVE NOT THE
FAINTEST ENVY OF OUR WHIRRING FOOD-MIXERS. FOR A
WHILE THEY HAD A FIELD DAY AS WE THREW OUT OUR OLD,
LOVINGLY CAST, HAND-CRANKED FOOD GRINDERS IN FAVOUR OF
ELECTRIC ONES, AND THESE ARE CERTAIN TO BE IN USE FOR AT
LEAST ANOTHER CENTURY. HERE WE SEE THE PREPARATION OF A
TASTY BOWL OF DANDELION AND DAISY SOUP.

GNOMES KNOW MORE ABOUT MUSHROOMS AND TOADSTOOLS THAN ANY OTHER PEOPLE IN EXISTENCE AND CAN TALK ABOUT THEM TIRELESSLY FOR HOURS ON
END. NONE OF IT MADE MUCH SENSE TO US, BUT IT WAS SOON CLEAR THAT MUSHROOMS MEAN FAR MORE TO GNOMES THAN FOOD OR FLAVOURING. THEY USE THEM
AS TONICS AND MEDICINES, AND WE WERE TOLD THAT ANY GNOME WHO DOES NOT GET A REGULAR DIET OF CERTAIN TOADSTOOLS FALLS SICK AND JUST FADES AWAY
IN THE END. SO THEY SPEND A LARGE PART OF THEIR TIME CULTIVATING MUSHROOMS AND TOADSTOOLS, NOT JUST IN POTS LIKE THIS BUT ALSO IN THE WILD WHERE
THE CONDITIONS ARE JUST RIGHT.

ᎶᏁᎾᎷᎬ ᎶᎪᎡᎴᎬᏁᏚ

Gnome Gardens BEING ORIGINALLY WOODLAND FOLK, GNOMES ARE NATURAL GARDENERS AND REPAY TOLERANCE FROM HUMANS BY MAKING THEIR GARDENS FLOURISH. GARDENERS WHO SUSPECT A GNOME HAS MOVED IN WITH THEM SHOULD OBSERVE CERTAIN RULES OF ETIQUETTE IF THEY WISH TO AVOID SCARING THEM AWAY. MOST IMPORTANT IS NOT TO MENTION YOUR SUSPICION TO ANYONE OUTSIDE THE HOUSEHOLD.

THIS TINY FELLOW ASSURED US THAT HIS IS THE MOST COMMON SIZE FOR GNOMES. ONLY, HE SAID, THEY ARE THE LEAST NOTICED JUST BECAUSE THEY ARE SO SMALL. HOW RIGHT HE WAS HAS BEEN IMPOSSIBLE TO DETERMINE, HOWEVER, BECAUSE ALL GNOMES SEEM TO THINK THEIR SIZE IS NORMAL. POSSIBLY BECAUSE MOST OF THEM DON'T TRAVEL MUCH THEY ALL ASSUME THEY ARE THE NORM, AND VISITORS ARE TOO POLITE TO TELL THEM OTHERWISE.

SCALE CAN BE DECEPTIVE. IT IS NOT IMMEDIATELY OBVIOUS HERE, FOR EXAMPLE, THAT THE HOUSE IN FRONT OF WHICH THIS STOUT PAIR OF NORTH AMERICAN GNOMES IS STANDING IS NOT IN FACT THEIR OWN, BUT BELONGS TO THE HUMANS IN WHOSE GARDEN THEY LIVE.

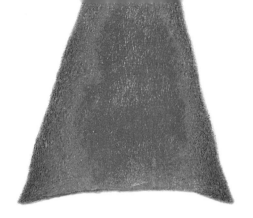

Gnomes do not mind too much if their
garden's owners suspect their presence (as long
as they are suitably discreet and respectful and
accidentally-on-purpose leave the odd treat out) but if
they start talking about it to their friends, the gnomes will
immediately up sticks and move away. Also it is best not to
complain at any unexpected mess in the garden shed. Gnomes
are not very tidy when it comes to borrowing our tools and are
likely to be offended at complaints, given how much they do to keep
the garden itself in order.

What gnomes appreciate are little gifts of food and drink that are not made too
obvious. Also they like privacy, which means not having a glaring spotlight playing
on your garden all night. Given these things, they will happily work away on your
behalf, helping everything to grow, keeping the weeds and pests in order and making sure
the bindweed doesn't strangle your carrots.

They are also very loyal in guarding the garden from intruders and will do everything to trip them
up or otherwise scare them away. Rakes will mysteriously slide into just the spot where their foot is
about to come down. Piles of flowerpots will crash as they pass and bats will fly into their faces. They
might even see worrying shadows move in the bushes and hear the growling of a non-existent Alsatian
nearby. In theory a determined thief might ignore all these things and the gnomes would in the end be powerless
to stop him, but burglars are rarely that brave. Most intruders are all too ready to believe that something horrible
might happen to them at any moment.

Gnome methods of gardening are largely a matter of instinct. They don't need to study books or hang on the words of some
ancient master to learn the tricks of their trade (although they often do both anyway just because they enjoy it). Most gnomes
simply have a natural instinct for what is needed to make a garden grow the way they want it to. The plants and soil talk to them
directly in a way we cannot begin to understand. It is like a kind of music striking on to a sixth sense that few humans possess in
more than a tiny measure. A garden to a gnome is like a constant, slow-changing symphony. Harebells really do chime, and so do all the
other flowers and plants in the garden. Each has its own particular song that tells how happy it is. The aim of a gnome in his perfect garden
is to create a unique symphony that is largely lost on humans because we can only enjoy the sight and scent of it.

GNOMES TAKE AS MUCH PRIDE IN THE TOOLS OF THEIR TRADE AS THEY DO IN THEIR OWN CHILDREN. WELL, ALMOST. OR NOWHERE NEAR AS MUCH REALLY, BUT THEY APPEAR TO. A GOOD FORK IS EXPECTED TO LAST A HUNDRED YEARS AT LEAST, SO IT COMES TO FEEL ALMOST PART OF THE GNOME. IF HE LOSES IT HE WILL BE INCAPABLE OF DOING EVEN THE SIMPLEST TASK FOR DAYS, AND IT TAKES WEEKS TO WORK HIMSELF UP TO HAVING TO GET A NEW ONE. THIS INVOLVES A JOURNEY TO THE NEAREST GNOME BLACKSMITH WHO IS LIKELY TO LIVE MILES AND MILES AWAY. THEIR WORK IS SO LONG LASTING THAT THEY SERVE A WIDE AREA.

SO ALL IN ALL LOSING A FORK OR SPADE IS A SERIOUS MATTER FOR GNOMES. THEY WILL OFTEN BORROW HUMAN GARDEN TOOLS BUT TREAT THEM AS MERE IMPLEMENTS, MUCH AS WE DO – PURELY A MEANS TO AN END. THEIR OWN TOOLS GENERALLY HAVE NAMES LIKE SODBUSTER, WORMBITER OR APHID BANE, AND GET PASSED ON AS HEIRLOOMS WITH AS MUCH REVERENCE AS VIKING SWORDS.

GNOMES DO NOT JUST CULTIVATE FLOWERS FOR THEIR PRETTINESS OR BEAUTY. THEY APPRECIATE THESE THINGS AS MUCH AS WE DO, BUT OTHER FACTORS SUCH AS SCENT OR MEDICINAL VALUE COUNT FOR JUST AS MUCH. THE SCENT OF CERTAIN FLOWERS IS TO GNOMES AS UPLIFTING AS A DRAUGHT OF WINE, BUT WITHOUT THE SLIGHTEST DANGER OF A HANGOVER. THE MINGLED SCENTS OF A FRESH SPRING DAY IN A PERFECT GARDEN CAN SET THEM DANCING FOR SHEER JOY.

They can also, of course talk to hedgehogs, moles, snails, insects and all the other creatures one finds in a garden. Not with words, as children like to imagine, but as clearly as the creatures talk to each other, if that makes sense. When a bee, say, flies to its hive and performs the complicated song and dance that tells the others where to find a particularly succulent flower, a watching gnome will understand it as clearly as any bee in the hive. When a chick has fallen out of its nest, gnomes will rush to help its parents in the rescue.

PLANTS ARE A GNOME'S CHIEF INTEREST IN A GARDEN, BUT THEY LOOK AFTER ALL THE CREATURES THERE, TOO, ENCOURAGING THE HELPFUL ONES AND DISCOURAGING THE OTHERS. HERE WE SEE A GNOME CHECKING THE TEMPERATURE OF THRUSH EGGS DURING A SURPRISE LATE APRIL SNOWFALL. THE GNOME AND ROBIN WILL TRY TO KEEP THEM WARM ENOUGH TILL THE MOTHER RETURNS. GNOMES ARE TIRELESSLY HELPFUL IN SUCH WAYS AND ALL THE SMALLER ANIMALS TURN TO THEM AT NEED. SOME OF THE LARGER ONES, TOO.

gnome habitats

Gnomes' taste in gardening varies enormously. Some like neat, formal gardens and these are the gnomes most likely to set up home alongside humans in the suburbs where their handiwork is less likely to be noticed. One of the surest ways of telling when a gnome has moved in is the behaviour of the snails in your garden. Gnomes have a great affection for snails, and snails repay this by only eating plants that the gnome allows them to. So one sign of a gnome having moved into your garden is that your snails suddenly take to eating only the weeds and not your precious seedlings. For the more succulent flowers they noticeably start to stray next door.

Many gnomes like suburban or country gardens but some still prefer the wild woods, which under their care take on a special beauty that looks accidental but is noticeably different to the places where nature has been left to run riot of its own accord. We have all at some time stumbled on such spots, some glade or spring or stream that looks perfectly natural, and certainly untouched by human hand, but is as pretty as a picture and charmed with a feeling that takes us back to childhood.

The chances are that gnome gardeners have been at work, encouraging certain plants to grow and others to keep in their place, balancing the strong against the weak and particularly encouraging those herbs such as wild garlic that they like to use in their cooking. The New Forest in the south of England is particularly full of such spots because it supports a thriving population of gnomes.

Still other gnomes, perhaps a little surprisingly, have taken enthusiastically to the decaying areas of many large industrial cities, especially those with Victorian factories and mills with canals winding through them. Overgrown canal towpaths and railway cuttings offer endless chances for gnomes to set up home without being noticed; whole communities often spring up right under the unsuspecting noses of rushing human city-dwellers.

ONLY IN THE HIDDEN VALLEYS OF SWITZERLAND ARE SUCH GRAND GARDENING SCHEMES AS THIS POSSIBLE. GNOMES ARE VERY FOND OF THE MAZES WE BUILD AS WELL, HOWEVER, AND WILL USUALLY LEND A SPECIAL HAND TO KEEP THEM IN TRIM. OCCASIONALLY THEY WILL SWITCH THE PASSAGES TOO, JUST TO KEEP US ON OUR TOES. IN THE OLD DAYS GNOMES WERE VERY FOND OF LEADING PEOPLE ASTRAY BY BUILDING INVISIBLE MAZES THAT TRAPPED THEM AS THEY WALKED HOME IN THE DARK. IN THE WEST OF ENGLAND THEY WILL TELL YOU THAT NOT LONG AGO THIS WAS EVEN KNOWN TO HAPPEN DURING THE DAY.

THERE'S MANY A TALE OF SOME FARMER TRAPPED OR 'PIXIE-LED' IN HIS OWN FIELD IN PLAIN SIGHT OF THE WAY OUT BUT UNABLE TO FIND IT TILL SOMEONE COMES TO RESCUE HIM. THIS IS THE ORIGIN OF THE WORD 'PIXILLATED', MEANING THE STATE YOU GET INTO WHEN YOU DRINK TOO MUCH. THE EFFECT IS MUCH THE SAME. GNOMES ASSURED US THAT THIS SORT OF TRICK HAS NEVER BEEN THEIR DOING, THOUGH. IT'S JUST THOSE FLIGHTY CORNISH PISKIES, THEY WILL ASSURE YOU, OR ELSE GOBLINS. BUT THEY LOOK A BIT SHIFTY AS THEY SAY THIS, SO WE HAVE OUR DOUBTS.

gnomes and pests

Gnomes and humans have many gardening tastes in common, but there are big differences. The main one is of course over the use of chemicals. Gnomes are not against them in principle because they have some pretty toxic tinctures of their own for controlling pests. The difference is that most of our pesticides seem like biological flame-throwers to them, wiping out everything in sight. Gnomes are not above poisoning pests that threaten to overrun or destroy a garden, but it is a very last resort. Most of their potions are designed simply to discourage them from settling there in the first place; and they always allow a few to linger, just to preserve the natural balance of the garden. This is one of the things that give a gnome garden its special charm.

Snails and dandelions are two of the greatest banes of human gardeners in cool climates, but gnomes happen to be very fond of them both. Not only do they love dandelions as a flower and for the way they scatter their seeds like fairies on the breeze, they also love dandelion wine and use the plant in endless cooking recipes.

This is fine in pastures and woodland where nature sees to it that dandelions do not get out of hand. But dandelions look upon a suburban garden much the way a hungry pack of real lions looks into a valley full of dozy antelope. Suburban gnomes do not like to see them running wild in a garden any more than we do, but they will encourage them in odd corners where it does not matter, such as behind the shed. Or in the gardens of hostile neighbours.

It's best not to fall out with neighbours who have gnomes in the garden because the chances are the gnomes will take their hosts' side and send all kinds of minor horticultural plagues your way. Their tricks are never really malicious, but they can make for a lot of extra hard work.

Similarly with slugs, snails and caterpillars, gnomes say they are all needed in a certain measure for a garden to chime properly (though even gnomes can only tolerate pale slugs in tiny numbers). They have a special affection for snails and probably tolerate them far more than human gardeners, though they are also quite strict with them. Delinquents who persist in eating the wrong flowers get ticked off severely and often leave the garden in shame. Mostly they get along famously, however, and gnomes often ride snails like chariots around the garden as they make their tours of inspection.

GNOMES ARE PASSIONATELY FOND OF ALL FLOWERS, BUT THE TULIP IS AMONG THEIR FAVOURITES. WHETHER THIS IS A CAUSE OR EFFECT OF THERE BEING SO MANY GNOMES IN THE NETHERLANDS IS UNKNOWN, BUT WHAT IS CERTAIN IS THAT TULIPS FLOURISH SO WELL THERE BECAUSE GNOMES ENCOURAGE AND CARE FOR THEM. SOME GNOMES DEDICATE THEIR WHOLE LIVES TO TULIPS AND THERE IS A POPULAR NOTION AROUND THAT THEY ARE ACTUALLY BORN IN THE FLOWERS. THIS IS JUST A MISCONCEPTION ARISING FROM A COMBINATION OF THEIR HABIT OF FALLING ASLEEP IN THEM, MADE DROWSY BY THEIR SCENT, AND HANS ANDERSEN'S TALE OF THUMBELINA. SHE WAS INDEED BORN FROM A MAGIC TULIP BUT WAS NOT A GNOME AT ALL.

GNOMES CONSIDER THE DANDELION TO BE OUR MOST UNDERESTIMATED HERB. WE'RE SURROUNDED BY DANDELIONS AND HAVE KNOWN FOR CENTURIES OF THEIR ABUNDANT GOODNESS YET WE DETERMINEDLY SEE THEM AS NOTHING BUT A NUISANCE TO BE SCOURGED FROM OUR GARDENS. THEY EVEN TASTE QUITE PLEASANT IN TEA AND SALADS IF YOU PICK FRESH LEAVES, ESPECIALLY IN SPRING AND SUMMER. CHILDREN APPRECIATE DANDELIONS OF COURSE BECAUSE OF THEIR BRIGHT CHEERFUL YELLOW FLOWERS AND BLOW-AWAY TOPS. THE FLYING SEEDS REMIND THEM OF DANCING FAIRIES. THE DANDELION HAS WOKEN MANY A CHILD'S EYES TO THE WONDERS OF NATURE AND THE GNOMES' WORLD.

THERE MUST BE SOME KIND OF LESSON TO BE DRAWN FROM THE FACT THAT SO FEW OF US CARRY THAT EARLY LOVE OF THE FLOWER THROUGH INTO ADULTHOOD. GNOMES, HOWEVER, LOVE THE FLOWER COMPLETELY AND EITHER EAT OR DRINK IT IN SOME FORM JUST ABOUT EVERY DAY. THEY SAY WE'D BE MUCH HEALTHIER IF WE DID THE SAME. IT IS PERHAPS NO COINCIDENCE THAT DANDELIONS FLOURISH IN THE SAME PARTS OF THE WORLD AS GNOMES, NAMELY EUROPE, NORTH AMERICA, AUSTRALIA AND NEW ZEALAND.

THE SMALLEST GNOMES OFTEN RIDE ON THE BACKS OF SNAILS. PURELY FOR FUN OF COURSE, AS A MEANS OF GETTING FROM ONE PLACE TO ANOTHER SNAILS ARE ONLY MARGINALLY BETTER THAN NOT GOING AT ALL. GNOMES ENJOY RIDING SNAILS FOR THAT VERY REASON. IT SLOWS THEM DOWN. GNOMES LIVE VERY RELAXED LIVES COMPARED WITH US BUT EVERYONE IS MANIC COMPARED TO SNAILS. SO GNOMES FIND IT REFRESHING SOMETIMES TO OBSERVE THE WORLD FROM A SNAIL'S POINT OF VIEW.

THERE IS A SIMILAR POINT TO SNAIL RACING, WHICH WE MENTIONED EARLIER AS A POPULAR SPORT. ONE OF THE RULES IS THAT NO PROMPTING BY THE RIDER IS ALLOWED BEYOND THE GENTLE TWEAK OF AN ANTENNA OR THUMP ON THE SHELL. THE TROUBLE WITH SNAILS IS THAT THEY ARE UNABLE TO HOLD NEW THOUGHTS FOR LONG. SOON THEY BEGIN TO IMAGINE THESE THINGS HAPPEN TO THEM ALL THE TIME AND STOP PAYING ATTENTION. THEN THEY USUALLY WANDER OFF AT A TANGENT IN SEARCH OF FOOD, TOTALLY IGNORING THE SUCCULENT LEAVES LAID OUT AT THE FINISH LINE TO TEMPT THEM THAT WAY. MORE OFTEN THAN NOT THE PRIZE GOES TO THE LAST RIDER LEFT ON THE TRACK, ALL HOPE OF A CONVENTIONAL FINISH HAVING BEEN ABANDONED.

Gnomes also love caterpillars and cannot understand how humans seem not to have grasped the connection between caterpillars and butterflies. They hear us complaining about how few butterflies we see any more, then going off and drenching the begonias with a lethal cocktail that wipes out yet another batch of hopeful flutterers. Caterpillars in gnome gardens are trained the way snails are to spare certain plants, or at least spread their appetites around so that no one plant suffers real damage. They are also encouraged to stick to weed patches where they are safe.

So while there are areas of disagreement, on the whole gnomes get along very well with human gardeners and are happy to potter around the edges of our work keeping everything trim, fitting in with our ways and repairing any damage we do in our clumsiness. They are far more tolerant of our ecological meddling than we probably deserve. Or maybe it's just that in our gardens and parks and nature reserves they see that some of us are at least trying to give nature room to breathe, and that is enough for them to turn a blind eye to our many failings. Left to themselves, gnomes would make all the world a garden. There would be no cars, planes or any of that kind of thing, but then again, perhaps they would be bored without us and the challenges we set them in trying to restore balance to nature.

The first thing one can tell about a gnome garden is that it is friendly and welcoming, not too tidy and not too wild. It is more ordered and artificial than any forest glade but there is something of the same magic, a captured spirit of the woodlands where all gnomes once dwelt. Gardens to gnomes are living works of art. We cannot hope to enjoy them as fully as gnomes themselves do, but we can still share the magic up to a point. So encourage those gnomes into your garden. Leave room for them to set up home and bring a little forgotten magic into your lives!

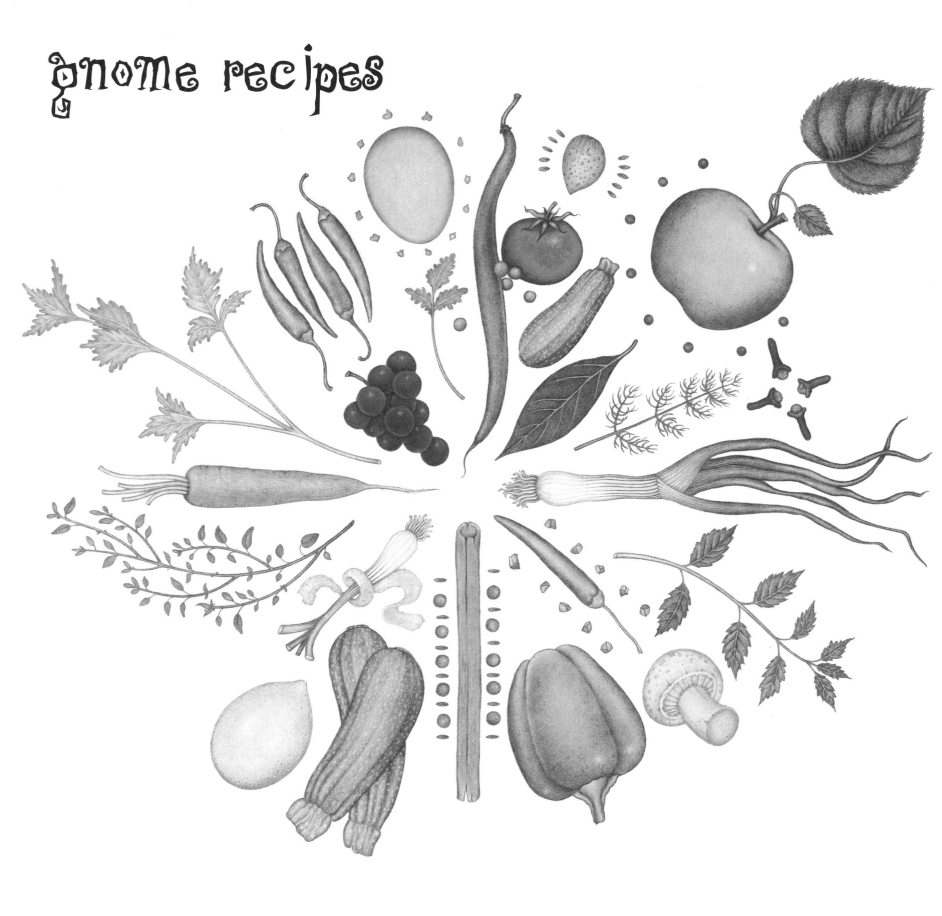

gnome recipes

gnome cooking

The following are a few typical gnome dishes using herbs that humans have almost forgotten, such as nettles and dandelions, as well as more common vegetables and herbs cultivated by humans.

The thing about gnome cooking is that gnomes see food as far more than just fuel to get them through the day. It's not just a matter of taste either. Their food is generally delicious but more than that it is health-giving. Our knowledge of nutrition is nothing compared to theirs. It is like comparing simple addition and subtraction to calculus. Gnome cooking is like their gardening, they aim for a symphony of nourishment that always keeps the body in perfect tune, which is why they are so healthy.

Gnomes use countless ingredients that we barely touch, or even turn up our noses at. It would take a book in itself just to scratch the surface of the subject but in the space we have here we have decided to concentrate just on dandelions. The dandelion is about the most common and despised gnome herb and is in fact as good for us as it is for them. It can be picked all year round except in the depths of winter.

Dandelions are best known for their diuretic effect. That is, they make you pee. They are in fact vulgarly known by varieties of the name Pissabed, so anyone who has a weakness that way should perhaps avoid them. But for most people the effect is barely noticeable and far outweighed by the benefits. Dandelion leaves and roots improve the secretion of bile, and are a great tonic for the pancreas and digestive system generally. They are rich in essential minerals, especially calcium, potassium and iron; they cleanse the blood and so are useful for relieving skin complaints such as eczema. Also, as a diuretic, dandelions can dramatically help reduce swollen joints and salt levels in the body. They also happen to have a quite sharp and pleasant taste, particularly in spring and early summer.

The simplest way of consuming dandelions is to chop up freshly picked leaves and petals into a lettuce salad, liberally sprinkled with lemon and salad dressing. Or they can be taken as a tea. This can be made with either fresh or dried leaves, using honey as a sweetener. Two teaspoons of finely chopped fresh leaves, or one of dried, should be infused with boiling water for five minutes before being strained. To dry the leaves, take a bundle and hang them upside down till the leaves just crumble away from the stem in your fingers, then store in a jar.

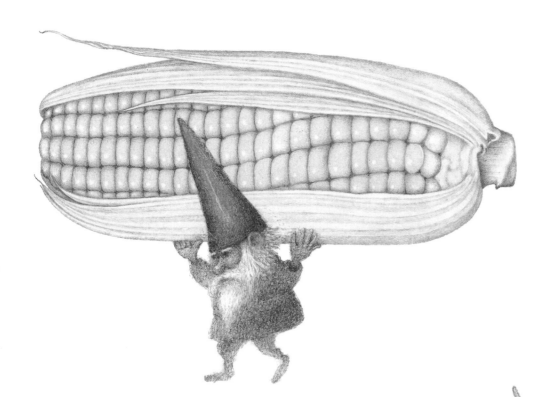

It's a curious thing but dogs and cats never interfere with gnomes when they sneak into our kitchens. Even the fiercest guard dogs just amble over to watch the goings-on with interest. This is a relic of the days when gnomes (or their forbears) regularly shared our houses. Deep down the animals remember and welcome the visitors. The only trouble is the washing up afterwards but often the animals come in useful there, especially dogs with long tongues and endless appetites. In large households the gnomes often don't bother because they know that in big families everyone always denies having made the mess that needs washing up.

Gnomes have fresh sweetcorn with almost every meal when possible. This keeps them very happy in parts of the world where it grows, but to many, given their longer time-scale, it is a recent novelty thanks to human imports. They will tell you when they first tasted sweetcorn, often down to the very day and what they were thinking of at the time, so great was the impression it made on them. For the smaller gnomes it also has the attraction of being divided up into handy meal-sized portions; Mother Nature's very own convenience food for gnomes, like peas and beans.

When picking dandelion leaves, care should be taken that they have not been sprayed with any chemicals. They should also be rinsed well just before use, to be on the safe side. Pick the youngest leaves and chop off the stalks. Caffeine-free coffee can be made from dried dandelion roots. These are best dug up in the spring or autumn when they are most plump and juicy. Scrub but do not peel. Dry in the sun and then roast at a medium heat until they are hard enough to be grated. Then percolate as with normal coffee. It is almost indistinguishable from standard coffee but with all the benefits mentioned earlier. Home brewers can make dandelion wine by adding seven or eight cups of dandelion petals to a gallon of apple or grape wine at the primary fermentation stage. The petals should be gathered when the sun is bright and the flowers fully open. They should be carefully separated from the flower heads, stems and leaves, which can make the wine bitter. Thoroughly rinse the petals and tie them into a fine straining bag suspended in the brew. For proper gnome wine you should use honey instead of sugar for fermentation, but this is up to you.

Fresh dandelion roots can also be diced, lightly fried, then stewed until soft and mixed with other vegetables. But tastiest of all is the gnome speciality, Dandelion Soup.

dandelion soup

Finely chop vegetables. Fry onion or leek in pan with butter for about 3 minutes. Add chopped potato, dandelion leaves, parsley & winter savory; fry until veg is soft (about 8 minutes). Add vegetable stock. Bring to boil. Add paprika, salt and pepper and simmer for 20 minutes. Blend in mixer. Return to saucepan to reheat. Add more milk if slightly thick. Pour into bowls adding a swirl of cream.

Serves 2–3

INGREDIENTS
1 oz butter
1 large courgette or zucchini
1 medium onion (or leek, according to taste)
1 large potato
2 oz fresh dandelion leaves
parsley and other herbs (plus winter savoury in season)
1 pint vegetable stock (stock cube plus half milk and half water)
dash of double cream
salt and pepper to taste (but go easy on the salt)
1/4 tsp paprika

The same recipe can be used in spring using nettle leaves instead of dandelions. New shoots should be picked (wearing gloves of course) and handled with care. They become totally safe after cooking. Nettles are a general tonic, being rich in vitamins and minerals (especially iron), and can relieve many allergic reactions including hay fever and nettle rash. After about June the leaves become too bitter for most tastes.

Special thanks to Linda and Roger Garland for their expert assistance in testing various gnome recipes on their trusting family. Sorry about that wild mushroom dish. Hope you all recover soon.

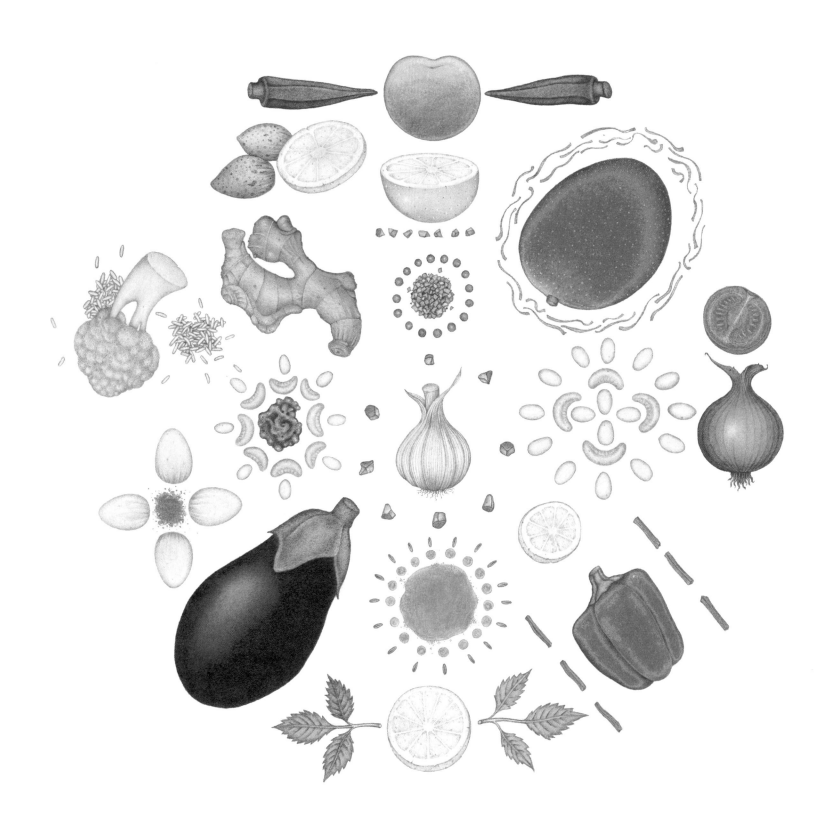

snail racing
two gnome board games

Gnomes play dozens of different games on the board overleaf by using different rules, which is why you find gnomes of all ages hunched over them. At festivals they often trace out a full-size spiral on the grass and act as the playing pieces themselves, with someone calling out the moves. Everyone joins in and winners often get to be king or queen for the day.

The first game, Singles, is one that gnomes start to play very young. It is a game of pure chance, much like snakes and ladders, which means they can play it against their parents on equal terms. More than equal terms in fact because, as everyone knows, the young of all species are naturally luckier than their parents. It is Mother Nature's little way of giving them an edge for survival.

The second game introduces an element of choice and therefore strategy, though it is still largely a game of chance. At the farthest extreme, gnomes play a game on this board that is like one-dimensional chess, a game of pure skill between two players.

In the example we came across they each have a king, queen and two pawns, which can move forward or backward by different amounts. The two sides line up facing each other across the central hole (the one with the double ring) and basically just hack their way through each other along a single track until one king emerges on the other side. We did briefly come into possession of the rules of this game, but sadly have both lost and forgotten them. It seemed to work. At least it managed to tie our brains in knots for a few evenings.

▶ riddle answers ◀

1. Book moth (or worm) · 2. In a dictionary · 3. The smallest
4. Hope (becomes hop, as in bitter beer) · 5. Bed · 6. Eyelids · 7. Splinter

RULES

singles (best with four or more players)

• Each player has one counter and throws a six-sided die to move, starting from the snail's head and aiming for the middle. The first to arrive is the winner.

• Whether an exact throw is needed at the finish is optional, but must be agreed at the start. If an exact throw is chosen, you have to sit waiting at the end till it comes up, you don't go in and out of the centre.

• If you land on another player, you send them back six places and take another turn. If the returning player lands on an occupied space, they must continue six more places until they find one vacant.

• If you land on a black space you have another throw. If you land on the double-ringed black space you have two more goes.

• If you throw a six you do not get a second throw unless for other reasons.

couples (best with four players)

• This is much the same as Singles but each player now has two pieces.

• You can move either piece. If one lands on the other, it moves to the space beyond (except when being sent back).

• A piece that lands on a black space must move next. You can never rest on black spots.

• The five spaces between the first two black holes in the spiral are now safe spots. If you are sitting on one you cannot be sent back. If at the start your throw lands you on one of these spots that is occupied (even by one of your own pieces) you cannot go.

• The winner is the first to get both pieces home.

threes (for three players)

• The same as Couples but you have three pieces. The winner is the first to get all three home.

• You need an exact throw at the finish.

fours (for two players)

• The same as Threes but the two players now have four pieces each.

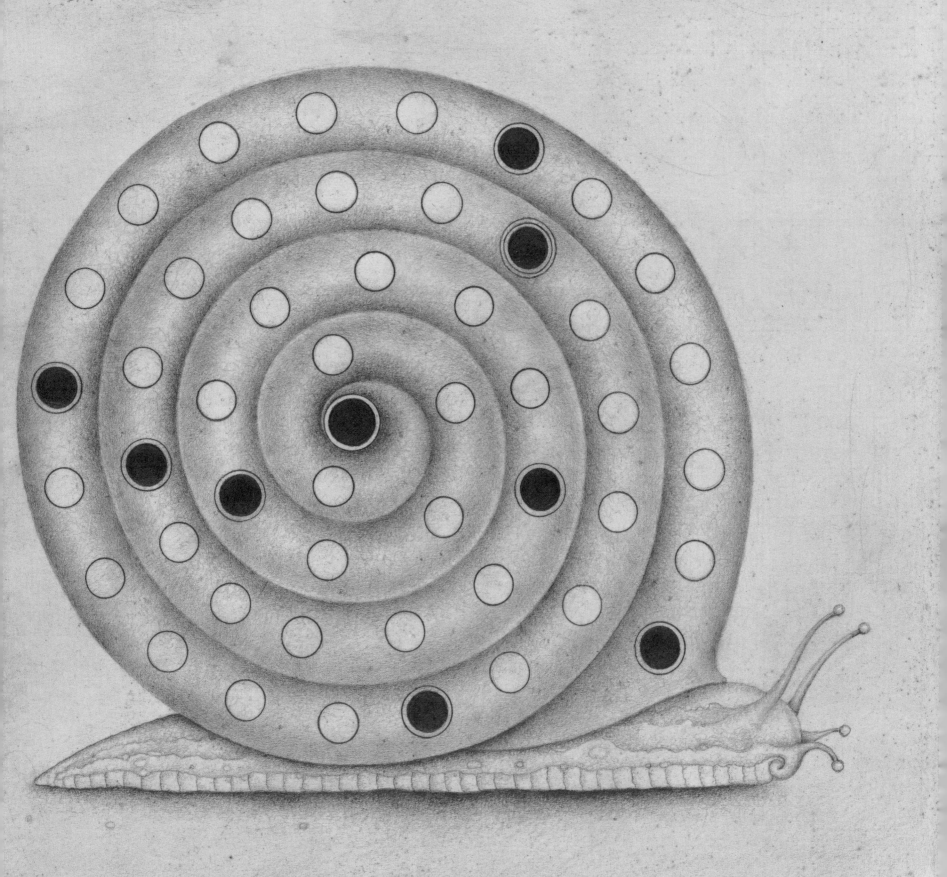

the end